Two Origins of Writing Systems, Discovery of the Number "0" and Our Numerals

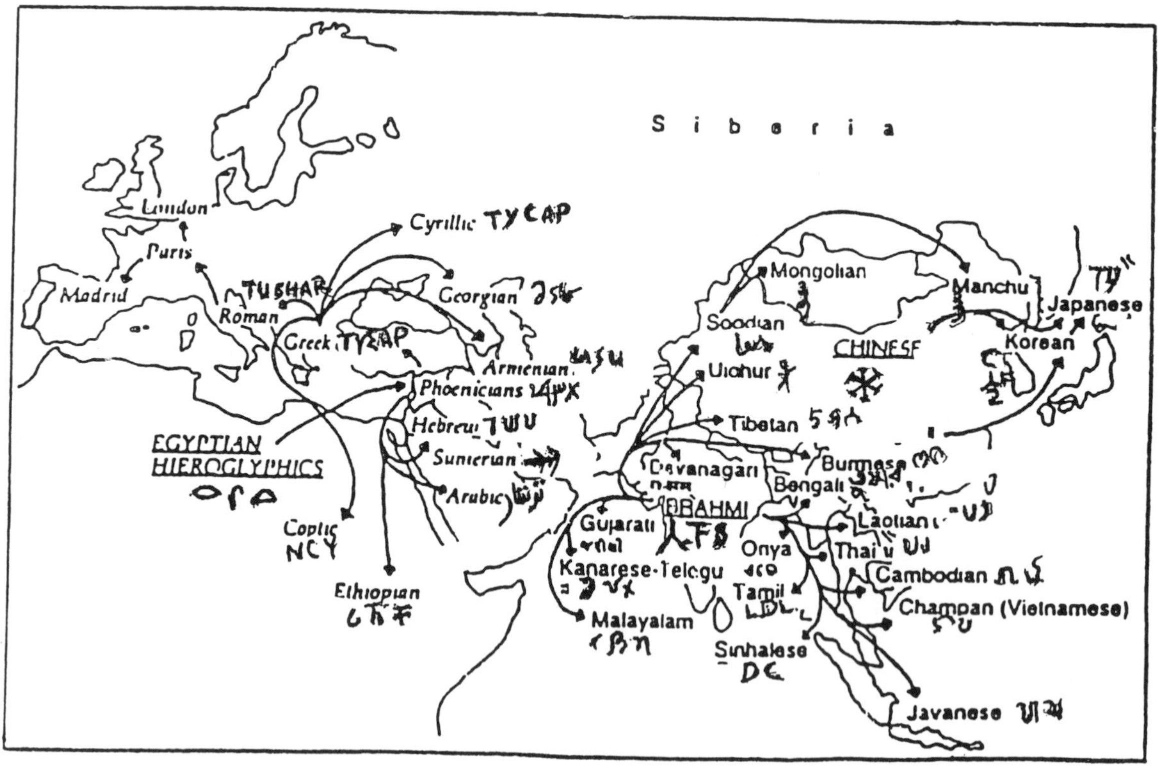

SCRIPTS OF THE WORLD : PHOENICIAN-GREEK, INDIAN BRAHMI & CHINESE

ORIGIN OF NUMBER "0" AND HINDU-ARABIC NUMERALS

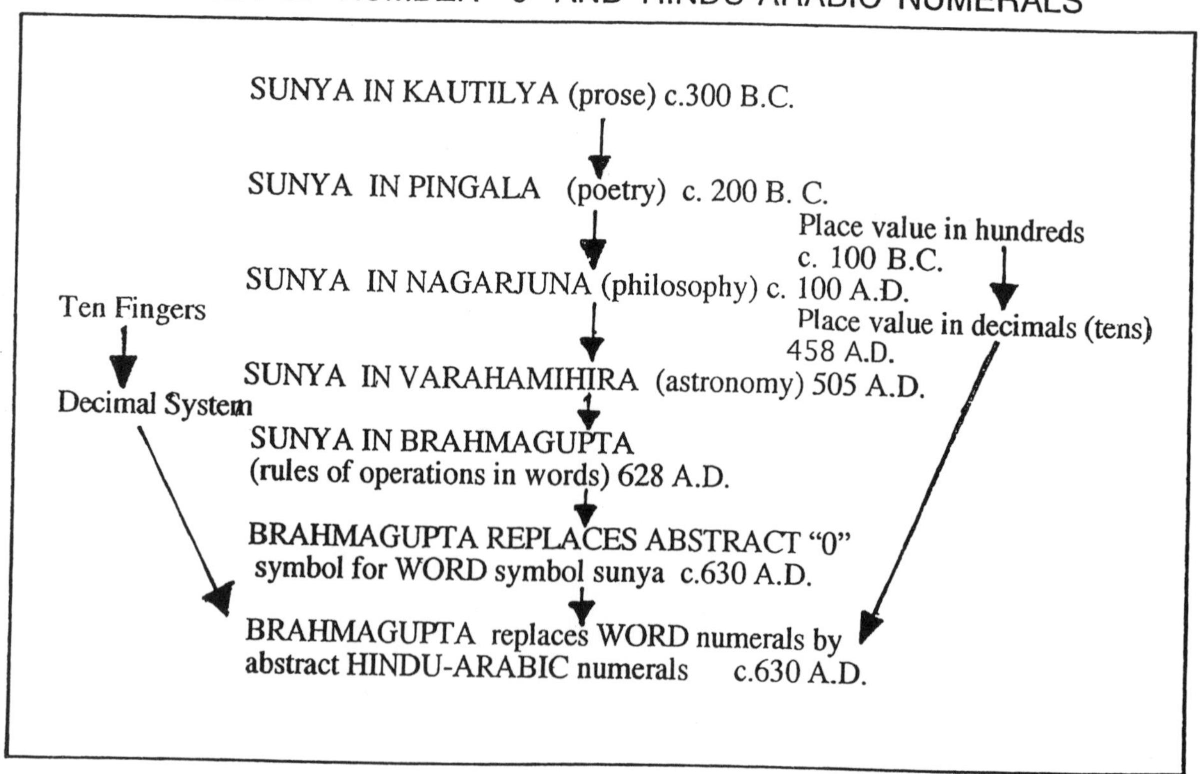

Two Origins of Writing Systems, Discovery of the Number "0" and Our Numerals

Dr. Tushar K. Nag

VANTAGE PRESS
New York

FIRST EDITION

Published by Vantage Press, Inc.
516 West 34th Street, New York, New York 10001

Manufactured in the United States of America
ISBN: 0-533-13653-9

Library of Congress Catalog Card No.: 00-92157

0 9 8 7 6 5 4 3 2 1

To my sons, Dev and Deepon

TABLE OF CONTENTS

Two Origins of Writing Systems, Discovery of the Number "0" and Our Numerals

INTRODUCTION

Learning the three R's: Reading, wRiting, and aRithmetic, is not only the basic right of all human beings, but is also essential for the maintenance and growth of modern civilization. Indeed, the three R's are among the most important elements in the origin of all civilizations. The importance of their usage is evidenced in daily life. This book is the first of its kind as it is on both writing systems and arithmetic. Although it is primarily written for the experts, for several important original discoveries, the book can be read profitably by any educated person interested in our civilization. The number of pages is deliberately kept to the minimum, in order to sustain readers' interest.

All scholars today believe that each and every writing systems developed from pictograms, which later acquired different sound values. It is surprising that none thought in the opposite way we use for over last 300 years: the phonetics of the unwritten languages are first analyzed, and then Individual signs are alloted for each sound. It is shown that in ancient times only the Indian Brahmi system for the Sanskrit language was created in the later method. Most western scholars believe that all alphabetic writing developed from the Phoenician alphabet, and there is only one origin of all the alphabets of the world. In constrast, Indian experts think that the Brahmi alphabet developed from the Indian pictographic Harappan (c. 2500-1700 B.C.) script. As we shall see, however, there are two fundamentally different origins of all alphabets. One developed from the picture signs which later acquired the sound values of the languages: this is the Egyptian-Phoenician-Greek group. By contrast, the Indian Brahmi system was created just the opposite way. The sounds (phonemes) of the Vedic Sanskrit language were first phonetically analyzed, and well over a century later abstract signs were allotted to each of the sound. In the Phoenician-Greek system of pictographic origin, the order of the letters (a, b, c, d, e, f,...) shows that the vowels and the consonants are mixed, and the letters are arranged without any phonetical order. On the other hand, in the Indian Brahmi system, the letters of the vowels and the consonants are invariably separated, and the order of the letters are arranged phonetically, for example, a, aa, i, ii, u, uu....separated from....k, kh, g, gh, c, ch, j, jh....etc. This difference in the order of letters appears, *without a single exception*, in the thousants of languages today, written in each of these two alphabetic systems.

The lower limit of the approximate date of the creation of Brahmi alphabet has been deduced from the date of the creation of the Old Persian script by King Darius (c. 500 B.C.), using the phonetical base of the Indian Brahmi system, and written in the cuneiform script of the Akkadians. The upper limit of the date has been estimated based on the phonetical analysis of the Vedas. The period and the location of the origin of the Brahmi alphabet has been determined on the basis of the economic, political, and cultural development as well as the intellectual revolt against Brahmanic religious orthodoxy in Magadha (Northeast India), later culminating in the religious movements of Buddha (566-486 B.C.) and others.

We have included more evidence for the acceptance of the Egyptian hieroglyphs, including 24 consonantal symbols, as consonantal alphabetic system in spite of numerous silent signs. Most scholars believe that the Indian and the Asian writings are syllabic; however, we have proven them to be alphabetic. Evidence is given that most alphabetic writings of Asia belong to the Indian system, and not the Semitic, as is now believed. There are over 20 figures and maps to help understand the text.

The credit for inventing the first writing system undoubtedly belongs to the Sumerians. However, the Sumerian syllabic cuneiform system, and its offshoots, did not survive beyond the first few centuries A.D. Therefore, the Egyptian-Phoenician-Greek-Roman writing system, borrowed by hundreds of languages and dominating the world today, is discussed first. Generally, most of the scripts are covered briefly. However, when discussing controversial themes, extensive explanation has been provided.

For the purpose of this book, arithmetic means calculation with numbers in writing, something everybody understands. No civilization would have developed without arithmetic. It is used today not only in our prosaic daily life, but in the sciences and mathematics, economics and commerce, engineering and technology, the social sciences, and in almost every aspect of our society. The abstract study of numbers, for instance the theory of numbers explored by Pythagoras (sixth century B.C.) through Srinivasa Ramanujan (1887-1920), is outside the scope of this book.

For well over a century many scholars have tried, unsuccessfully, to discover the origins of the Hindu-Arabic numerals, and the present day zero (0) as a number. The well known historian of mathematics, Professor David E. Smith (v. II, p. 69), has despaired: "There is no probability that the origin will ever be known." Brahmagupta of Ujjain, India, in his work *Brahma-Sphuta-Siddhanta* (628 A.D.), was the first mathematician to give the eight rules of operation on the *sunya* (zero) with results; as all numbers must have to function in arithmetic. As we will show later, he also replaced the *sunya* with the abstract symbol '0' taken from the redundant old Indian abstract symbol for twenty. One of his formulas, among others, that "the sum of affirmative and negative, if they are equal, is naught," meaning, for example, x + (-x) = 0, or 20 + (-20)= 0, showed for the first time objectively that the value of his zero is undoubtedly "nothing," the "0" is independent, and outside the numerals, for example, as a result of computation. Functionally and visually identical to the present number "0," the one that came into being around 630 A.D. is fundamentally different from the Babylonian, Greek, or the Indian *sunya* (zero) prior to Brahmagupta; not because the signs are different (ξ, o or *sunya),* but because the earlier zeroes could be used *only* as a gap-holder in the place-value numerals. On the other hand, Brahmagupta's "0" in abstract symbol could be used not only in the numerals, but also independently outside them to function in almost all branches of mathematics. This is the modern number "0" with its rules of computation. Soon after, Brahmagupta replaced the **word** numerals in decimal place-value with *sunya*, available in India since 458 A.D., by old Indian abstract symbols (1 to 9) and the newly discovered "0." Thus, Brahmagupta created the Hindu (Arabic) numerals in abstract symbols. We have also shown that the word numerals with decimal place-value and the *sunya* are far inferior to the abstract Hindu-Arabic numerals in every way, particularly in calculation.

Number means different things to different people. For instance, the great philosopher-mathematician Bertrand Russell said, "The number of a class is the class of those classes that are similar to it" (p. 20). In this book arithmetical numbers mean quantity (positive or negative), or no quantity (zero). Abstract number symbols are 1,2,3,4,5,6,7,8,9, and for the Indian zero, "0," representing no quantity. The "0" and the other numbers must have similar rules of operation, such as addition, subtraction, multiplication, division, square, square root, cube, and the cube root to function in mathematics. All numbers must have abstract symbols suitable for arithmetical calculation. Word numerals, even in ancient India, were rarely used in arithmetical calculations since they were very clumsy and inefficient. Instead, computations used to be done with the old Indian abstract numerals *without* place-value and the zero. These elaborate descriptions are essential to avoid confusion between the "0" as a true number we use today; and the first zero created by the Babylonians, used by the Greek astronomers with different symbols, and the Indian *sunya,* all used *only* in the numerals.

Part of the section on arithmetic is based on my book *Modern Civilization and Living Ancient Mathematics* (1990).

CHAPTER ONE

I. EGYPTIAN WRITING SYSTEM

Egyptian civilization probably began around 3,000 B.C., just one hundred years after the Sumerians. The great Greek historian Herodotus admiringly said that the Egyptian works of art were great beyond expression. His comment that Egypt is a gift of the Nile is well known.

In fact, Egyptian civilization was the gift of the ancient Egyptians, who were intelligent, imaginative, ingenious, industrious, and inherently artistic, creating powerful sculptures and architecture. As most of the papyri have vanished, and whatever writing has survived is mostly from mausoleums, we see a distorted picture of Egyptian life. Though it was thought that the ancient Egyptians were obsessed with death and after-life, Egyptologists over the century have revealed that they were more cheerful and happy than most other ancient peoples, and cultivated life could be maintained in peace and security (Neugebauer,71). During the yearly flood of the Nile River when cultivation was impossible, the peasants gave their labor to build pyramids and temples for their god-king Pharaoh, as during the Medieval Age the European farmers built their cathedrals. A physician described patients with injuries of the brain and spinal cord with symptoms, signs, diagnosis, prognosis and treatment as rationally as is done today (Smith Papyrus), the first scientific writing.

All writing systems have two facets: the visual signs and the internal phonetical structure. The latter is more difficult as it involves the phonetical analysis of the language. Based on the analysis, the decision is made whether to use only consonants, or both consonant and vowel sounds (phonemes), for the signs of the alphabet. In some orthographies there are signs for syllabic sounds, word signs (logogram), signs for meaning (determinative or key), and others, used as the unit for the writing system.

The Egyptians were keen and artistic observers of their surrounding environment. Almost from the beginning we see realistic pictures of numerous objects present in ancient Egypt, many of which all of us can recognize today. The Egyptian priests tried to use these pictures to write their language, at first visually, and later vocally. When they were only visual we call them "logograms," "word pictures" or sometimes "ideograms," for example, (☉) for sun; and when the pictures were vocalized we call them "phonograms" or "sound pictures," as a picture of bread (⌓) pronounced 't' in Egyptian language. At this stage Egyptians could not use the pictures for many vital aspects of their language, for example, abstract words, grammatical adjuncts, most names, particularly foreign names. Furthermore, thousands of words in the Egyptian language needed thousands of different pictures.

One of the earliest hieroglyphic writings was found in the Nar-Mer pallete, dating probably 2900 B.C. On this a picture of a catfish and a hammer were engraved ( ). In Egyptian, catfish is 'nar," and hammer is 'mer.' Using the sounds of the pictures of two objects, Egyptians could thus write the name of the king Narmer. This was a great breakthrough from the severely limited word picture writing to the true and complete writing system. Here, the symbols were used for other words with the same sound but different meaning (homophones). This method is called the rebus principle. The English equivalent would be to draw a picture of an eye and use the sound for the word 'I' (myself). There is no way one can draw a picture of '*I* .' The vocalization of the words also used for their homonymous word is often called phonetization. The Egyptians were the first to invent the acrophonic principle, which means the use of the first sound of the word-picture for the letters of the alphabet. For example, in the Egyptian language, 'net' means water, and its sign, , was used for the letter '*n* .' All Egyptian words started with consonants; they developed only consonantal alphabet by acrophonic principle. Sometimes they used pictures for allied concepts, for example, a picture of the sun ( ) for day or light. We do not know the name of the genius, perhaps a priest, who first used the rebus or the acrophonic principle in writing.

EGYPTIAN ALPHABET

The heart of the Egyptian writing system is the phonetized word-pictures with one, two or three consonants, representing faithfully the consonant sounds (phonemes) of the Egyptian language. There were 24 consonantal phonemes in the Egyptian language, and they used the same number of hieroglyphs for them in the alphabet, with one-to-one correspondence. Only phonemes 'y' and 's' had one alternative sign each. In the early stage of the Egyptian language the roots of many words had one strong consonant, usually at the beginning of the word, and one or two weak consonants. The weak consonants gradually fell away, and the strong consonants constituted many of the signs of the alphabet (Driver,134). For example, in ri, , mouth, only the strong consonant, r, was used as a character in the alphabet. Driver shows in his book (Fig. 80) how a third of the alphabet developed in this way. Some of the uniconsonantal words naturally supplied several characters of the alphabet; for example, , 't' means loaf. The rest of the hieroglyphs of the alphabet probably developed from words so far back in time that these words have passed out of the written language (Budge, 31).

Fig.1. EGYPTIAN ALPHABET

Signs	Sounds	Meanings	Signs	Sounds	Meanings
	'a	vulture		kh'	placenta
	y	reed		h	?
	'ain	hand		s	bolts
	w	quail		ṣ	cloth
	b	leg		sh	pool
	p	seat		q	hill
	f	viper		k	basket
	m	owl		g	jar-stand
	n	water		t	bread
	r	mouth		ṯ	rope
	h	house		d	hand
	kh	rope		ḏ	snake

These 24 characters of the alphabet were from the beginning indispensable in writing words which could not otherwise be expressed

(Fischer, 63). The words for primary grammatical function (prepositions, particles, demonstratives) were written purely in phonograms (in a number of cases, alphabetic signs) (Meltzer, 550). The alphabetic signs were most frequently used in the Egyptian writing system (Davies,11). The importance of the Egyptian alphabet lies in the fact that with only the 24 characters their language could have been written more or less adequately. But without the alphabet, even with all the hundreds of biconsonant, triconsonant signs, logograms, and determinatives, a full writing system for the language would have been difficult.

MULTICONSONANTAL SIGNS

The Egyptians had about 90 biconsonantal and 40 triconsonantal hieroglyphic characters during the Middle Kingdom. Just over half of these were frequently used. Probably all of them were phonetized word pictures with two or three consonants. As the hieroglyphs were accurately drawn pictures of common objects, most of the Egyptians could recognize many of the pictures and knew their names. The direct visual-phonetic relationship of each character of the hieroglyphs, and the sound (names of the objects) in the Egyptian language were their great asset, and unique in the history of writing. For example, the picture of a 'lute' as the sign ( ) in their writing, and the word 'nefer' in the Egyptian language meaning lute, and its homophonous word meaning 'good,' were known to most Egyptians, the illiterate and the literate. Similarly, a stylized picture of a house ( ) 'per' also meant 'to go'; and further, a picture of a swallow was read as 'wer,' meaning a swallow as well as big. English equivalents would be to draw a picture of a head, which could mean, in context, intelligence, authority; a picture of a fox may also indicate cunning or scheming which cannot be drawn in pictures.

The great advantage for the Egyptians to have their writing in recognizable pictures, and corresponding names in familiar words, along with their homophonic words, is obvious. This means that a child or an illiterate person with minimal teaching, or with a few hints, could learn their words. Once they learned the technique, they could use it on their own on most of the hieroglyphic characters they encountered. Therefore, the Egyptians needed to learn only some unfamiliar but frequently used hieroglyphs, specifically, stylized pictures. Of course, they had to know how to organize their hieroglyphic signs in words to represent their language.

Almost all the hieroglyphs with one, two or three consonants represented the consonant sounds of the Egyptian language probably fairly accurately. The scribes naturally preferred to use the hieroglyphs with two or three consonants instead of two or three separate alphabetic hieroglyphic signs. This is reasonable, since one multiconsonantal hieroglyphic picture is easier to learn, read, write, understand, and more economical than two or three separate alphabetic hieroglyphs. For these advantages they had to learn probably over 90 commonly used hieroglyphs, although many of them were pictures of familiar objects known to them.

VOWEL SIGNS

The Egyptians at an earlier stage did not invent any separate signs for their vowel sounds. Around 2000 B.C. they started using their weak consonants for their vowel sounds which gradually increased until the Nineteenth Dynasty (1303-1200 B.C.). During these centuries there was intensive foreign contact, and to transliterate exactly the names of the foreign rulers and lands, the signs for the vowel sounds were needed, and their use was systematized (Gelb, 169). For example, *Twnip* was used for the Syrian city Tunip; *Pwtwhip* for the queen PutuHipa (ibid). In this way they used the three weak consonants, ' , w, i, for the vowels a, u, and i respectively (Ibid). Unfortunately, they did not continue to use the vowel signs to the end, which was a mistake. However, Egyptian being an Afro-Semitic language, their consonantal skeleton of each word, usually three in number is invariable, similar to the Arabic or the Hebrew. In contrast, the sounds of the vowels change according to grammatical rules. For any Egyptian it was natural to pronounce correctly in context the vowels in the words. The Arabs and the Hebrews without their vowel signs read their books and newspapers fluently. Even English, an Indo-European language 'cld b rd flntly wtht 'ny vwl sgns wth lttl prctc.'

WORD SIGNS (LOGOGRAMS, IDEOGRAMS)

In Egyptian they were pictures of familiar objects without phonetic values, for example, ⚲ , meaning 'sun' or 'day.' Usually a vertical mark was put under the picture to show that they are not pronounced. There were about 90 hieroglyphics in this category at any one time, only half of them were frequently used. The Egyptian logograms were familiar pictures, and Egyptians knew the words and their meaning directly from the pictures.

DETERMINATIVES (SIGNS FOR MEANING)

The Egyptians frequently used, at the end of each word, pictures which carried the specific or general meaning of the word. These signs are termed determinatives by the Egyptologists. They are silent and determine the meaning of the word. They are familiar pictures of man in different actions, women, animals, birds, plants, gods, goddesses, house-hold articles, and others. Most of them were well known to the Egyptians, and many are known even to us. Anyone who would like to see how many hieroglyphs one can recognize today should consult the monumental dictionary of hieroglyphs by Willis Budge. These pictures were easily learned and retained in memory for life by the Egyptians. There were about 300 pictures during the New Kingdom, less than half of which were used frequently. Since they were used at the end of the words, they also function as word separators. In ancient times writing was continuous, but gaps separate the words today.

"The habitual employment of absolutely useless signs" it has been noted, "is a conspicuous characteristic of Egyptian orthography" (Edgerton,485). Let us try to understand the hieroglyphic pictures through the ancient Egyptians' eyes. Imagine a scribe teaching the elementary hieroglyphs to several ordinary Egyptian boys, not in a scribal school. The scribe was as conscientious as his counterpart today, trying to teach the writing system to a class including the most inattentive, forgetful, and dull students. The teacher first drew the 24 pictures of the alphabet, and many students recognized the familiar pictures. He asked the students to pronounce them loudly, and most of them did. He taught the stylized and other hieroglyphics not known to the students. The same routine was repeated with the commonly used familiar pictures of biconsonantal and triconsonantal words. He also showed that the same picture often has more than one meaning (homonyms), which was also known to many students. The teacher, still was not sure that everyone would remember the multiconsonantal characters or their sounds, told his students to repeat the last one or two sounds by using relevant signs of the alphabet; we call these 'phonetic complements.' He also told them never to pronounce these hieroglyphs, and gave examples of what would happen if they did. A house, 'per,' would sound like 'perper,' 'heper' (beetle) would sound like 'heperper,' or 'nefer' (lute) may sound like 'neferfer.' These would sound ridiculous to every Egyptian. Similarly in English to write and pronounce X with phonetic complements such as 'Xs,' or 'Xz,' would be equally funny. Even then the scribe was not satisfied that the meaning of the word was clear to all the students, so he put at the end of the word, a picture that gave the specific or the general meaning of the word, particularly in homonymous words. Then the teacher taught them how to organize the characters to make a word. These silent hieroglyphs, namely, the logograms, phonetic complements, and particularly the determinatives certainly helped to clarify the sounds and the meanings of the words to other Egyptians rather than confuse them.

"In the Egyptian language," there was a "wealth of words with the same consonantal framework. The ambiguity resulting from writing with letters could be removed with the additional word signs" (Jensen, 63). Furthermore, "the ideograms and determinatives were a help, not a hindrance, to understanding." (Diringer, v. I, p. 33). Moreover, "with the use of word picture signs the script became more attractive and more vivid, and through its richness provided the opportunity of all sorts of allusions and association of ideas" (Schmitt, quoted by Jensen, 63). The Egyptian orthography had far more memory devices than any other writing systems of the world. An average Egyptian could hardly make mistakes in reading and understanding the meaning of simple words and sentences. It seems that the Egyptian scribes were never sure that others would understand the sounds and the meanings of their writing, so they tried to give as many clues as possible, often unnecessarily. The Egyptians also used a large number of unnecessary logograms. Many determinatives in the form of familiar pictures were excellent for clarifying the meaning of some homonymous words. Here also the Egyptians showed their lack of restrain by using hundreds of them, often where they were not needed.

For ordinary Egyptian children and adults, reading and to a less extent writing the basic hieroglyphic system probably was not as difficult as we think. Particularly because they knew the sound and the meaning of the hieroglyphic pictures, and learning the non-phonetic elements under some guidance was not hard. Memorization of most of the known hieroglyphic pictures would have been simple for an ancient Egyptian.

For the students who were studying to be professional scribes, things were quite different. The school texts suggest that the students were taught the hieretic script before the hieroglyphs: The pervasiveness of the word-pictures as a mnemonic (memory) unit provides evidence that word recognition, rather than a sign-by-sign spelling or analysis, was typical the way writing was taught (Meltzer, 61). They also were taught to write complete words or phrases without analyzing the component signs in cursive hieretic with ligatures. (Williams, 219, q. by Meltzer, 61). Furthermore, Meltzer (43) believes that the "Egyptian writing (and education) emphasized word-recognition and multifaceted word characterization in which an incomplete phonetic representation was supplemented by (and even subordinated to) visual and mnemonic priorities." The scribes had to learn the irregularities of their writing, the intricacies of the grammar, and their literature. They also had to be proficient in arithmetic, algebra, and geometry with various applications, the religion and history of Egypt, art, medicine, and other diciplines. Unfortunately, the Egyptians did not use the everlasting clay tablets like the Sumerians, so most of the writing on papyri have perished.

Egyptian hieroglyphs are the most majestic and beautiful writing ever devised. Artistic scribes, however, were not that abundant even in artistic Egypt. Also, the speed required for everyday writing could not be done in hieroglyphs. Therefore, the Egyptians designed the cursive hieretic signs for rapid writing, wisely retaining the hieroglyphs to the end. In our computer age, writing a few hundred hieroglyphs is not a problem; the Japanese currently handle thousands of characters. Moreover, the Egyptians generally kept the phonetic signs separated from the nonphonetic ones; even when they were combined, their relationship remained recognizable. If they had put them together in one character, as did the Chinese or the Mayans, there would have been thousands of characters instead of scarcely more than 400 hieroglyphs (Fischer, 65) in use at certain period.

The Egyptians organized their characters into words, as is done in English, but not in a linear way. Art played an important role, with respect to the size and location of the characters in a word. The literacy rate of ancient Egyptians was certainly very low not because of the large number of hieroglyphs but because the idea of universal education was unknown in all ancient civilizations. We will see in another chapter that the literacy rate in ancient Greece at the height of their civilization was also low even with alphabetic writing.

It is often asked why the hieroglyphs continued for almost 3,400 years even when Egyptians developed cursive hieretic and the demotic. This is because the hieroglyphic writing system was far superior to the cursive writings in every way except for speed. Hieretic writing, though originated from the hieroglyphs, lost most of the practical advantages of the familiar pictures of the hieroglyphs while continuing the defect of large number of nonessential characters in hieroglyphs. Around the sixth century B.C., when the highly cursive and clumsy demotic script (people's script in Greek) developed, the Egyptian civilization was gasping for breath; it was losing all its vigor and creativity.

Why did not the Egyptians use only the 24 consonantal alphabetic hieroglyphic signs and discard all other signs for the multiconsonantals, logograms, phonetic complements and the determinatives? Then the 24 consonantal hieroglyphic alphabet would have been similar to the Arabic or the Hebrew writings? If they had continued to use some of the weak consonants as vowels signs, as they did during the second millennium B.C., their orthography would have been almost comparable to the average writing for the European languages. How much a part did conservative attitude play in preserving all the non-alphabetic hieroglyphs? No civilization in history has drastically changed its nationally developed writing system by itself. Even the English, who borrowed their writing system from the Romans, failed to improve significantly the English orthgraphy. At the dawn of civilization, the Egyptians had only the Sumerian model, and no systematic study of phonetics or writing systems was available to them. Now there is a plethora of models and examples of all the writing systems, including the International Phonetic Association's (I.P.A.) alphabet. Still they have virtually no beneficial effect on the English and many other orthographies.

Did the Egyptians create an alphabet? Of course they did, with 24 signs for 24 consonant phonemes in a one-to-one correspondence between the signs and the sounds (with only two exceptions). Diringer (v.I,33), however, denies this by saying that in true alphabets each sign generally denotes one sound only, and each sound is represented by a single constant symbol, and even if the Egyptians acquired an "alphabet," they did not know how to use it. With this definition Diringer is excluding the English, French, and many other orthographies of the world as alphabetic. If English and the French have alphabetic orthographies with many redundant, silent, and misleading use of characters, then the Egyptians certainly also had an alphabetic writing system. If the early Semitic, Phoenician, Hebrew, and the Arabic orthographies without vowel signs are considered as alphabetic, then so, too, should the Egyptian. Furthermore, the Egyptians used three weak consonants, *'a, i, u,* as vowels for several centuries, as we have already discussed.

Deciphering the Egyptian hieroglyphs was extremely difficult. At first the pictures were thought to be pictograms without any phonetic values. Eventually, the Swedish diplomat Akerblad, the Englishman Young, and specially the French scholar J. Fr. Champollion, were convinced that many of the Egyptian pictures represent the sounds of Egyptian language. The Rosetta stone which was found in 1799, now is in the British Museum is inscribed in hieroglyphs, demotic, and translation in Greek; it was the greatest help in deciphering the sound values of the hieroglyphs, particularly the cartouche containing eight hieroglyphic characters. Champollion correctly guessed that the hieroglyphs in the cartouse represent the name of some important personanity. He searched for an important name in Greek translation in the Rosetta stone, and found the name PTOLEMIOS which was not in a cartouce. He correctly decoded the hieroglyphs as for the sounds: PTOLMYYS. (From right to left).

Champollion used the hieroglyphs for the P, T, and L in PTOLMYYS to find out the name of KLEOPATRA also in a cartouche. He also confirmed his correct interpretation on other hieroglyphs carved on rocks.

The major problem was that none expected that the Egyptians had added to their alphabetic characters, the logograms, biconsonantals, triconsonantals, phonetic complements, and the determinatives. The scholars did not know that the Sumerians and the Chinese also used the "sound and meaning" elements in their writing. Furthermore, nobody knew the ancient Egyptian language, although Champollion knew its descendant, the Coptic language. However, in 2500 years there was considerable change in the language. What was not too difficult for the ancient Egyptians was extremely complex and confusing for modern scholars.

The Egyptians invented the concept of the rebus along with the Sumerians, and alone the acrophonic principle. Without these two great inventions, a full writing system could not have developed in the fertile crescent area.

II. PHOENICIAN-GREEK WRITING SYSTEM

During the second millennium B.C. several civilizations in the Eastern Mediterranean area developed writings influenced by the Egyptian writing system. Probably the earliest of these was the Minoans on the island of Crete. Excavation in Crete by Sir Arthur Evans revealed the Royal palace with beautiful wall frescoes and other evidence of a prosperous civilization. The Minoans also developed a writing system inscribed on large vases and clay tablets which is preserved as they were burnt by foreign invaders. We call their writing "Linear A." Many of the signs were borrowed from the Egyptian hieroglyphs and later simplified. The Minoan language is not known, the scripts are not yet deciphed.

Evans, finding another type of script in Crete, named it "Linear B." The second system of writing was deciphered by a brilliant Englishman, Michael Ventris, an architect, who was interested in the writing of Crete, and attended at the age of 14 a lecture on it by Evans. Ventris, using code-breaking techniques on the Linear B writing, found the language to be indeed archaic Greek. He later collaborated with John Chadwick, a specialist in archaic Greek. They found that this script was borrowed from the Minoan script, the Linear A, with which many of the signs are identical or nearly so (Chadwick, 27). The script is syllabic with five vowel signs, and separate signs for 60 syllables, all with a consonant followed by a vowel (CV), for example *ka, ki, ku, ke, ko.* There were about 22 ideograms (logograms). Later the same writing system was found in Mycenae on the mainland of Greece, and this writing system is also called Mycenaean script. Of course, the Greek language has too many syllables for only 65 signs, so Mycenaean script was inadequate for it.

Recently, in the desert beyond the valley of the Kings near Thebes, Egypt some inscriptions were found by Professors John Coleman and Deborah Darnell, carved on softstone dated 19th or 18th century B.C. This may be the earliest evidence of the consonantal alphabet, and the characters are inflenced by the Egyptian writings. Some of the characters resemble the Canaanite characters curved by the turquoise miners on a statue which Sir Flinders Petrie discovered in 1905, and Sir Alan Gardiner deciphered it in 1915 A.D. These characters on the statue are (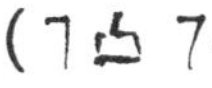 lb'lt) which translates [dedicated] "to the lady," meaning the Canaanite goddess Asherah, equivalent to the Egyptian goddess Hathor (Cross, 79-80). Since then similar characters have been found in Syria and Palestine. In these old Canaanite inscriptions about 28 different consonant letters were found. From these characters 22 letters of the Phoenician alphabet developed, of which about 20 signs can be traced from pictures (Ibid, 80). Other short scripts were discovered close to the Mediterranean coast of Syria, Lebanon, Israel, and Sinai peninsula. Byblos, in Lebanon, was a great trading center through which large amounts of papyri passed, and some specimen of writing were found there. The city of Ugarit on the north coast of Syria, another major trading center, also developed an interesting writing system. Throughout the area, except in Ugarit, the inhabitants were probably Canaanites, a Semitic people, centered around the cities of Tyre and Sedan. The Phoenicians were their descendants. They dominated the sea trade on the Mediterranean, and had colonies throughout the area, most famous of which was the city of Carthage in Africa. We know almost nothing about their civilization from their writing; they extensively traded papyri, on which they used to write, and all of which have perished. Whatever little we do know came from their neighbors. King Solomon apparently requested King Hiram to send skilled architects and carpenters to help build the most important temple of the Hebrews. The Canaanites were great navigators and builders of large ships which roamed throughout the Mediterranean Sea. From the Romans we know how great was the military leadership of Hannibal, who took an army with elephants about two thousand miles, even across the Swiss Alps to fight the Roman Army. From the Greeks we know that they borrowed their script from the Phoenicians. In what other aspects of civilization they excelled is not known.

The Phoenicians' or their forefathers' greatest contribution to mankind is the creation of a consonantal alphabet with only 22 letters, with one-to-one correspondence between the sign and the sound of their language. There is no doubt among many scholars that they were greatly influenced by the Egyptian writing. Gelb (147) thinks that the 24 uniconsonantal hieroglyphs are identical in inner structure with the 22 to 30 signs of the different Semitic group. However, their borrowing, unlike most others was highly sophisticated. They took the acrophonic principle from the Egyptians and used the stylized pictures of objects familiar to them. For example, in Egyptian water is 'net,' and using the acrophonic principle they had 'n' ( ) in their alphabet. In the Canaanite language water is 'myannar,' and by using the acrophonic principle they adapted the same sign ( ) as 'm' in their alphabet. Sampson wondered why the Canaanites took so much trouble, as it would have been simpler to borrow the signs along with the sound of the Egyptians. The borrowing would have been easier, and that is the way most borrowing is done (78). However, there was some advantage for the Canaanites to learn and remember the names of the letters in their language, rather than in Egyptian. The Canaanites showed great insight into the Egyptian writing system, and they intelligently used the similar system in their script for their people to learn the alphabet easily. They also had no emotional attachment to the Egyptian tradition, and being a practical trading people, they could reject the logograms, phonetized words with two or three consonants as well as all the determinatives, probably the most drastic and useful modification in the history of writing. They naturally designed only 22 letters for their 22 consonantal sounds as most borrowers do. It is surprising that they did not take the idea from the Egyptians of using the weak consonants for their vowel sounds. The Canaanites used a Semitic language, and the roots of most words, as in the Egyptian, were consonants. For the Canaanites it was much easier to guess the vowels in context than in any Indo-European language. Still it was a defect, and all the writing systems without vowel signs eventually developed signs for vowels. The Phoenicians failed to create vowel signs, most probably because they used the acrophonic principle, and as their words always start with consonants; so they got only consonantal characters from the initial sound of their words, like the Egyptians. More than half alphabetic scripts of the world except for the East, South, and the Southeast Asia derived from the Phoenician script.

Several other scripts developed in this area, including the interesting Ugarit alphabet for the people on the north coast of Syria. They took the technique of pressing the stylet on soft clay tablets to write in cuneiform script from the Babylonians, but they did not take any particular sign from them. Their characters were much simplified. However, the inner phonetic structure was almost identical with the Old Semitic-Phoenician alphabet. They had 27 consonant and three vowel signs, 'a, 'i, and 'u,' as early as the 14th century B.C. For the first time in history we find the order of the letters in an alphabet in the Ugarit abecedary :

'a, b, g, h, d, h, d, h, w, z, h, t, y, k, s, l,
m, d, n, t, s, ', p, s, q, r, t, g, t, 'i, 'u, s.

If we drop several letters not used in English we will find that our a, b, c, d,....are basically arranged in the Ugaritic way. This shows that both alphabets originated from the same source, in spite of differences between the Cuneiform and the Roman scripts. We will see later that the order of the letters is extremely important in deciding the source of the alphabets. As the alphabet is sometimes used as numbers, the order of the letters has to be strictly maintained.

The South Semitic alphabet first appeared at about the end of the second millennium B.C. (Diringer, v.1,174). It might have developed from the Proto-Sinaitic but the evidence is inadequate. Diringer (Ibid,179) says "It is difficult to see a direct relationship between the North and the South Semitic alphabets, though it may be the only instance of alphabetic writing not descended from the North Semitic."At the same time he agrees with G. R. Driver that it is unlikely independent invention with similar symbols occurred at the same time by the two branches of the same race. A close look at the order of the letters in these two alphabetic systems strongly suggests either a common origin, or one deriving from the other. The upper half of the North Semitic abecedary is somewhat similar to the lower half of South Semitic, and *vice versa.* This is the most drastic change in abecedary in the history of writing systems. Fig. 2.

North Semitic (upper half) South Semitic (lower half)	'A, B, G, D, h, H, w, z, h, T, Y 'A, d, G, D, g/b, T, z,d, Y, T, s/z
North Semitic (lower half) South Semitic (upper half)	K, s, L, M, d, N, ts', P, S, Q, R, T h, L, h, M, Q, w,S, R, b, T

The Ethiopic script derived from the South Arabic, as the signs and the order of the letters clearly followed the South Arabic alphabet. Because Ethiopians had difficulties in representing their language without vowel signs, like all other Semitic writing, diacritical marks for vowel differentiation were borrowed from India around 350 A.D. (Gelb,188); indeed there were trade relations during this period between these two countries (Ibid). Ethiopic signs are not syllabic, as is now believed, but have 31 consonant characters, with six diacritical marks representing six different vowels, a, u, i, a , e, o, always attached to the main consonant characters. The consonantal characters can always be recognized although attached to diacritical marks for the vowels. The Ethiopic script has no individual syllabic characters. They also took from India the idea of pronouncing consonants with a short /a/ sound instead of the names of the animals or the objects used by the Semitic people. Unfortunately they did not take the individual vowel signs from the Indian Brahmi system.

The Arameans were a Semitic tribe who settled in Syria and Mesopotamia around the 12th century B.C. They borrowed their writing system from the North Semitic. The characters are mostly similar to the North Semitic and the Phoenician, and the order of letters are the same. The Assyrians conquered the Aramaic land, around 8th century B.C. deporting the people throughout the Assyrian empire. However, the Aramaic people and their language flourished, and later became the *lingua franca* for the entire empire. Under the Achamenid rule it became, with Persian, one of the official languages of the Persian Empire, the usual language for traders from Egypt to India. For more than a thousand years it was the vernacular of Israel; it was the mother tongue of Jesus Christ and the Apostles, and probably the original language of the Gospels (Diringer, v. i, p.198). In Kandahar, now in Afghanistan, an inscription in Greek and Aramaic was found dating 259/258 B.C. extolling King Ashoka's religious and governmental principles.

From the Aramaic, several alphabets descended, including the Arabic and the Hebrew. The origin of the Arabic alphabet is controversial. Some scholars believe that it came from Nabataean and that the date is 328 A.D, while others think that it came from the Syriac. The Arabs took 22 signs from the Semitic alphabet and designed six more. The amount of writing in Arabic characters is scanty until the Koran was written. Earlier, they followed the order of letters from the Semitic but later modified it by putting similar letters in groups. The Arabic Alphabet (right to left direction): Fig.3.

ر r	ذ dh	د d	خ kh	ح x	ج j	ث t	ت t	ب b	ا a
ف f	غ gh	ع '	ظ z	ط t	ض d	ص s	ش sh	س s	ز z
	ى y	و w	ه h	ن n	م m	ل l	ك k	ق q	

The Arabic alphabet spread along with Islam to extensive areas in Western Asia, Northern Africa, Central Asia, Persia, Afghanistan, Pakistan, in India (for Urdu language) and the Malay peninsula. The last one was replaced by the Roman; and the Uzbeks, Kazaks, Turkmens, Tadziks and the Kirgiz people replaced the Arabic alphabet with the Cyrillic. Turkish used to be written in the Arabic alphabet but its own leader, Kamal Ataturk, replaced it with the Roman alphabet. The Arabic alphabet is used by more people than any other alphabet except the Roman.

The Hebrews at first wrote their language in Phoenician characters, but by the 9th century B.C. they had modified the characters to make their own alphabet which lasted for three centuries. In the second century B.C. they developed from the Aramaic the "Square script." The Hebrews ceased to speak in their language a couple of centuries before Christ and used the Aramaic language instead. However, Rabbis continued to use Hebrew and the square script; when Israel was born the Hebrew language was virtually dead, existing primarily in religious books. Incredibly, however, the book language was revived as a spoken language, a unique phenomenon in the history of languages. The script has 22 letters, all consonants as in other North Semitic alphabets. Later it developed diacritical marks like other Semitic scripts, indicating different vowels. "Hebrew letters are not distinctive," observes Sampson, "letters resemble one another much more than Roman letters do" (94).

THE GREEK ALPHABET

We have already discussed that the Greeks borrowed a syllabic writing system from the Minoans around 12th or 13th century B.C. The second time, between the 10th and 8th centuries B.C. they borrowed the script from the Phoenicians acording to Greek tradition and called them *Phoinikeia gramata* (Phoenician letters). The shape of the letters, name of the signs, and the order in the alphabet are almost identical. The earliest epigraphic evidence of Greek writing is around 740-730 B.C. Scholars differ on the date placing it from the 11th to 8th century B.C. The location of borrowing is controversial, varying from the Syrian town of Al Mina to mainland Greece. The way the Greeks borrowed the alphabet is also disputed. L. H. Jeffrey wrote a thoroughly researched book on the early Greek script, thinks that the Greek traders, with no idea of writing, first encountered the Phoenician merchants' writing in the Phoenician alphabet. The Greeks took the signs, the names, and the sound value of the letters of the alphabet without deliberate alteration or rejection. The borrower will equate the sound value of the doner with a somewhat similar sound in his own language, although to a modern philologist the sound may be quite different.(p.3). DeFrancis (178) supporting Jeffrey's idea says, the Phoenician write a symbol and utter a word that starts with what we might describe as a "coughed *ah* " sound, made with a sudden closing of the air passage (glottal stop). "To the Phoenicians the coughed aspect is important and marks the sound as consonant. To Greek ears it sounds like a funny way of pronouncing what is to them a sort of *a* sound." DeFrancis adds, "In much the same way as the vowel *a* came to be represented, so also the symbols for the remaining vowels resulted from the Greek mishearing Phoenician consonants as Greek vowels." (Ibid). Sampson (101) shows his doubt, "Some scholars have supposed that this was a result of a conscious plan by a clever Greek scribe, I feel sceptical about the idea. It seems easier to imagine the reinterpretation of the letters as having happened automatically as a consequence of the learning of the letters name and the acrophonic principle by the speakers of a language with a non-Semitic phonological system."

On the other hand Diringer (359) strongly disagrees with Jeffrey's method and conclusion, saying, "No Semitist will be able to agree, for instance, that the Semitic 'alef, he, 'ayin resemble the Greek sound a, i, o." Professor Diringer certainly does not believe that about 3,000 years ago a Greek expert in Semitic phonetics existed in Greece. Driver (154) says, "It was natural that yod (y or i) and waw (w or u) should be taken for i and u since they are related to the vowels." Coulmas (164) writes, the Greeks pronounce the name of the first letter of the Phoenician alphabet not with a glottal stop as the Phoenician would but with an initial vowel. The result was that they added the letter alpha as a genuine vowel sign to the Phoenician consonant script." Coulmas added that "other consonant letters of the Phoenician inventory that assumed vocalic quality in Greek were *he* for Greek epsilon /e/,*waw* for /w/ which later became /u/;*Yodh* became /i/ and *'ayin* became /o/. Coulmas continues, "In word final position most of the letters had already been used as *matres lectionis.* In Greek the application of the device was extended and systematized" (Ibid). Jensen (453) just described without any comment from which consonant letters Greek vowel letters originated. Gelb (181) summerizes the origin of the Greek vowels:

> The Greeks did not invent a new vowel system but simply used for vowels those signs which in the various system of writing likewise can function as vowels in the form of the so-called *matres lectiones*. The greatness of the Greek inovation lies, therefore, not in the invention of a new method of indicating vowels but in a methodical application of a devise which the early Semites used only in an irregular and sporadic fashion. As we have seen, the Semitic and other Near Eastern writing in the course of time developed this method of indicating vowels to such an extent that they, too, were on the way towards a full system of vowel signs and consequently an alphabet.

We have already mentioned that the Egyptians during the second millenium B.C. used three vowel signs for writing mostly foreign names. The Ugarites also used the vowels a, i, u in the 14th century B.C. We may conclude based on the leading scholars on the borrowing of the Greek alphabet that the Greeks took the Phoenician alphabet in the usual way borrowing is done. However, the Greek alphabet had a profound effect on the orthographies of the world. It is the model for the Cyrillic alphabet for Russia, and countries of Eastern Europe carried by the Greek Orthodox Church in the 10th century A.D.. The Romans adapted the Greek alphabet through the Etruscans. As the Romans dominated much of Europe, the Roman Catholic Church spread their alphabet to most of the continent. Furthermore, since West Europeans have dominated the world since the Renaissance, the Roman alphabet spread all over the world, except in Asia, Eastern Europe, and North Afica.

How accurately did the Greek and the Roman alphabets represent their phonemes of their respective languages? Allen (1991, p.10) says that the post-Euclidean spelling of Greek comes near to phonemic: the principal shortcoming in the vowels, failure to distinguish short and long a, i, υ , and in the consonants, the use of special symbols to represent some combination of two phonemes, viz. χ Ks, and ψ ps. Number of consonant phonemes in classical Greek language was from 14 to 18 (Ibid, 9).

Allen believes, Latin had 15 to 18 consonant phonemes in native words. Latin spelling is close to completely phonemic; the only defect in Latin orthography is that it does not distinguish for the long and short vowels. (1965, p, 9).

The Greeks introduced upper (Capital) and lower (small) cases of scripts with definite rules of application. All the scripts derived from the Greek also have two sets of scripts. However, rules of application for the upper and lower case varies according to the tradition of that particular language. The Germans use capital letters more than others. Coulmas (258) shows the inconsistency in understanding the idea of noun, giving it a circular definition, "a word that is spelled with a capital letter!", he continues, "most of the rather contrived examples are not very convincing." Two sets of scripts increase spelling mistakes as well as memorization. In contrast, the Brahmi and all the scripts derived from it have only one set of script, and they have no difficulty in recognizing a word after a period, name of a country, city or a person, beginning of a word in a poem, *et cetera.*

The development of the Greek, Roman, and the Cyrillic scripts from the Phoenician is shown in the next page.

Fig.4

PHOENICIAN		GREEK		ROMAN	CYRILLIC
Names (Meaning)	Signs	Signs	Names	Signs	Signs
'Aleph (ox)	𐤀	Α	Alpha	A	А
Beth (house)	𐤁	Β	Beta	B	Б
Gimel (camel)	𐤂	Γ	Gamma	C	Г
Daleth (door)	𐤃	Δ	Delta	D	Д
He	𐤄	Ε	Epsilon	E	Е
Waw (hook)	𐤅				
Zayin	𐤆	Ζ			
Heth (fence)	𐤇	Η	Eta	H	
Teth	𐤈	Θ	Theta		
Yod (hand)	𐤉	Ι	Iota	I	И
Kaph (open hand)	𐤊	Κ	Kappa	K	К
Lamed	𐤋	Λ	Lamda	L	Л
Mem	𐤌	Μ	Mu	M	М
Nun	𐤍	Ν	Nu	N	Н
Samekh (fish)	𐤎				
'Ayin (eye)	𐤏	Ο	Omicranon	O	О
Pe (mouth)	𐤐	Π	Pi	P	П
Sade	𐤑				
Qoph	𐤒			Q	
Res (head)	𐤓	Ρ	Ro	R	Р
Sin (tooth)	𐤔	Σ	Sigma	S	С
Taw	𐤕	Τ	Tau	T	Т

The Greeks added three extra signs, upsilon, chi, and omega, Υ , Χ , Ω , respectively. The Romans extended the signs, G, J, Q, V, Y, and Z. The Russians added seven extra letters.

Hundreds of languages all around the word are written in the Roman alphabet. Consonants in the Roman alphabet are more or less adequate for most of the languages. Among the exceptions is the Czech alphabet; new letters with diacritical marks were created to reflect the extra Czech consonantal phonemes. They are, č, ď, ň, ř, š, ť, ý, ž. However, only five letters for the vowel sounds are inadequate for almost all the languages. Spanish orthography has the reputation of almost perfectly representing the language - a claim the specialist John A. Green disputes. "The main cause is the preservation of etymological spelling. C and g have two pronunciations depending on the following vowel - cerca 'near' = /therka/ or /serka/, gigante 'giant' = /xigante/; h is never sounded;" and there are other etymological spelling. Green thinks that several spelling in Spanish "are not compatible with phonemic principles." According to Hammerstrom, quoted by Moss (137) there are 18 vowels in the French language, so they have to create 13 extra vowels with diacritical marks: à, â, ë, é, è, ê, ï, î, ô, oe, ü, ù, and û. Italian language have seven vowel sounds, with five letters they manage fairly well. Portugese language has 14 vowel sounds, they created 9 extra signs with diacritical marks on the five Roman letters for vowels.

English language has about 28 consonantal and 12 vowel phonemes. As it kept the spelling inherited from the Anglo-Saxon, Norman French, and many other languages without any significant changes for centuries, there are furthest deviation from the present English sounds. For the 12 vowel phonemes there are only five letters. The long vowel 'I' sound is written in 11 ways: m*e*, f*ee*, s*ea*, f*ie* ld, conc*ei* ve, mach*i* ne, k*ey* , qu*ay*, p*eo*ple, subp*oe*na, and C*ae*sar (Gelb, 224). Examples from the consonants are, the sound for /k/ is written as in cat, chorus, accost, acquire, liquid, saccharine, kettle, and check. Some letters are silent, for example, b in debt, l in salmon, s in Island, gh in dough, t in catch, and others. "The number of different spellings for the 40 English phonemes has been variously estimated at 600 (Zachrison,1931: 4)....to 2,000 (Daniels,1985: 34)" (DeFrancis,120). Furthermore, according to DeFrancis "100 *percent* of English phonemes are spelled more ways than one." (228).

The German language has 19 vowel sounds, including three diphthongs, and the number of consonant sounds are 21. However, German orthography faithfully represent the language. According to Brosnahan (quoted by Moss,132), the number of vowels in other Germanic languages are as follows: Dutch(12), Swedish (13), Danish (15), and Norwegean (15). The Scandinevians added three extra vowel signs with diacritical marks for each languages. Finnish, an Uralo-Altaic language like the Hungerian, uses the Roman alphabet. According to Branch (595), "The orthography of standard Finnish is for the most part phonetic; with two exceptions all sounds are marked orthgraphically. If a letter is written twice, it indicates that quantity is double the length of a single sound." There are eight short vowels, and each has a long counterpart. The consonant system has 15 phonemes and 13 letters. (Ibid, 597). The Finnish orthography is generally considered to be one of the most phonetical, however, it is far from perfect.

Many languages all over the world have replaced their old alphabet to Roman script. For example, Turkish, Bahasa Indonesia, Vietnamese, Tagalog in the Philippines are written now in the Roman alphabet; also the people's spoken languages in the Pacific Islands of Tahiti, Hawaii, Fiji, and others use Roman alphabet. Even in China Pinyin has developed in the Roman alphabet as an auxiliary to the Chinese characters. Most of the native languages of the Americas, for example, Maya, Quechua (Inca), and Aymara (Bolivia-Peru) as well as Navajo, Sioux use the Roman alphabet. The Hausa, Yoruba, and the Ibo languages in Nigeria, and Swahili in East Africa, have adopted the Roman alphabet.

The Cyrillic alphabet developed from the Greek alphabet introduced to Russia in the 10th century A.D. by the Greek Orthdox Church. The Russians made their orthography reasonably phonemic by adding seven extra letters to the Greek alphabet. The Cyrillic alphabet is also used for the Ukranian, Bylorussian, Serbian, and almost all the languages of Siberia as well as Russian influenced Central Asia, for example, Uzbek, Kazak, Tazik and others.

III. INDIAN WRITING SYSTEMS

The reverence the Hindus held for their sacred *Rg-Veda* (c.1500-1000 B.C.), the oldest literature in the Indo-European languages, should never be underestimated. The *Rg-Veda* was transmitted orally by Brahmin families for well over a 1,000 years. To preserve the purity of the Vedic Sanskrit language many grammarians and phoneticians arose, culminating in Panini (c. Fifth century B.C.). The doyen of the American descriptive linguists, Leonard Bloomfield, in his classic book, *Language*, said Panini's grammar "is one of the monuments of human intelligence,...no other language, to this day, has been so perfectly described" (p.11). Panini's grammar became the model, and the great European grammarians of the 19th century, such as Franz Bopp, Rasmus Rask, and Jacob Grimm, and subsequent grammarians, used his technique (Balmuth, 59). The Indian grammarians contributed significantly to the phonetics of the Sanskrit language.

Centuries earlier, the words related to phonetics existed in such non-technical works as the *Brahmana, Aranyaka,* and the *Upanishads* (c. Ninth and Eighth centuries B.C.). In these texts various phonetic categories were mentioned, such as "articular," "place of articulation," "stop," "fricate," "semivowels," "vowels," and "voice" in its technical connotation, writes W. S. Allen (p. 6), professor of phonetics at the University of London and an expert on the Sanskrit, Greek, and Latin phonetics. Since 800 B.C. a series of scholars have studied the phonetics of the *Vedas.* Allen says (p. 5), "The authors of our treaties were clearly phoneticians rather than priests, and a scientific curiosity, coupled with keen audition and an effective methodology led to the description ...There is a singular lack of religious dogmatism, and the authors refer to each others' opinion in a commendable objective manner. These earlier phoneticians speak in fact to the twentieth century." Furthermore, "without the Indian grammarians and phoneticians....it is difficult to imagine our niniteenthth century school of phonetics" (Prof. J. R. Firth, quoted by Allen, 3).

These phoneticians' works fall into two main categories, the more important and authoritative being the *pratisakhyas* (800-500 B. C.), dealing with the four *Vedas*, and the *Sikshas* (500-150 B.C.), which mainly supplement the former (Ibid, 5). The phoneticians, after analysis of the Sanskrit language, found 34 consonant sounds, which they arranged according to the origin of these sounds from the throat to lips: velar, palatal, retroflex, dental, and labial. Each of these groups was further subdivided on the basis of whether the sounds were unaspirated or aspirated. Moreover, "in the recognition of the voicing process the Indian phoneticians make one of their greatest contributions"(Ibid, 33), and they classify the voiced separately from the voiceless consonant sounds. In Europe, "only in the later part of the nineteenth century, under the influence of Indian teaching, does the recognition of the voicing process make headway" (Ibid, 37). The phoneticians organized the semivowels as well as the fricatives (voiced and voiceless) in the order of origin from the throat to lips. They arranged the vowels separately from the consonants and put both of them in phonetic order. The long and short vowels were paired, and dipthongs (compound vowels) were put at the end of the vowels.

There was no writing system for the Sanskrit language at that time, and the works on the phonetical analysis were carried on orally along with the *Vedas* exclusively by the Brahmins. The great grammarian Panini almost certainly knew the Brahmi alphabet, as evidenced by his mention of *akshara* (letters) several times in his masterpiece *Astadhyayi;* but, "he was too great a grammarian to be influenced by the alphabet" (Ibid,15). Also, his order of vowels and consonants was a little different, as he adopted the phonological approach, as opposed to the phonetic method used by earlier phoneticians.

The earlier phoneticians' model of the vowels and consonants was the internal phonetic structure of the Brahmi system of writing. Probably, a century later, a phonetician designed the abstract individual signs for each of the 14 vowels, and 34 consonants, in the order the phoneticians had already constructed. This method of creating an alphabet was unique in ancient ages. However, all modern linguists follow this method to create a new alphabet for any language without a script, then find out all the different sounds of the particular language and, finally, assign an individual sign for each sound.

Was the inventor of the Brahmi alphabet aware of the existance of any other people writing their speech? This is quite probable. The nearest one was the cuneiform characters of the Akkadians, about 3,000 miles away; the Aramaic and the Chinese were further away. However, he did not know any particular one; otherwise, the influence would have shown in the Brahmi system both in the phonetic base and the script. Could it be a type of "stimulus diffusion," the way Egyptians were supposed to be influenced by the Sumerians? Most probably he knew that other people were writing their languages, but he went on designing individual signs in simple geometrical forms for each of the *Vedic* Sanskrit sound.

Fig. 5. BRAHMI ALPHABET

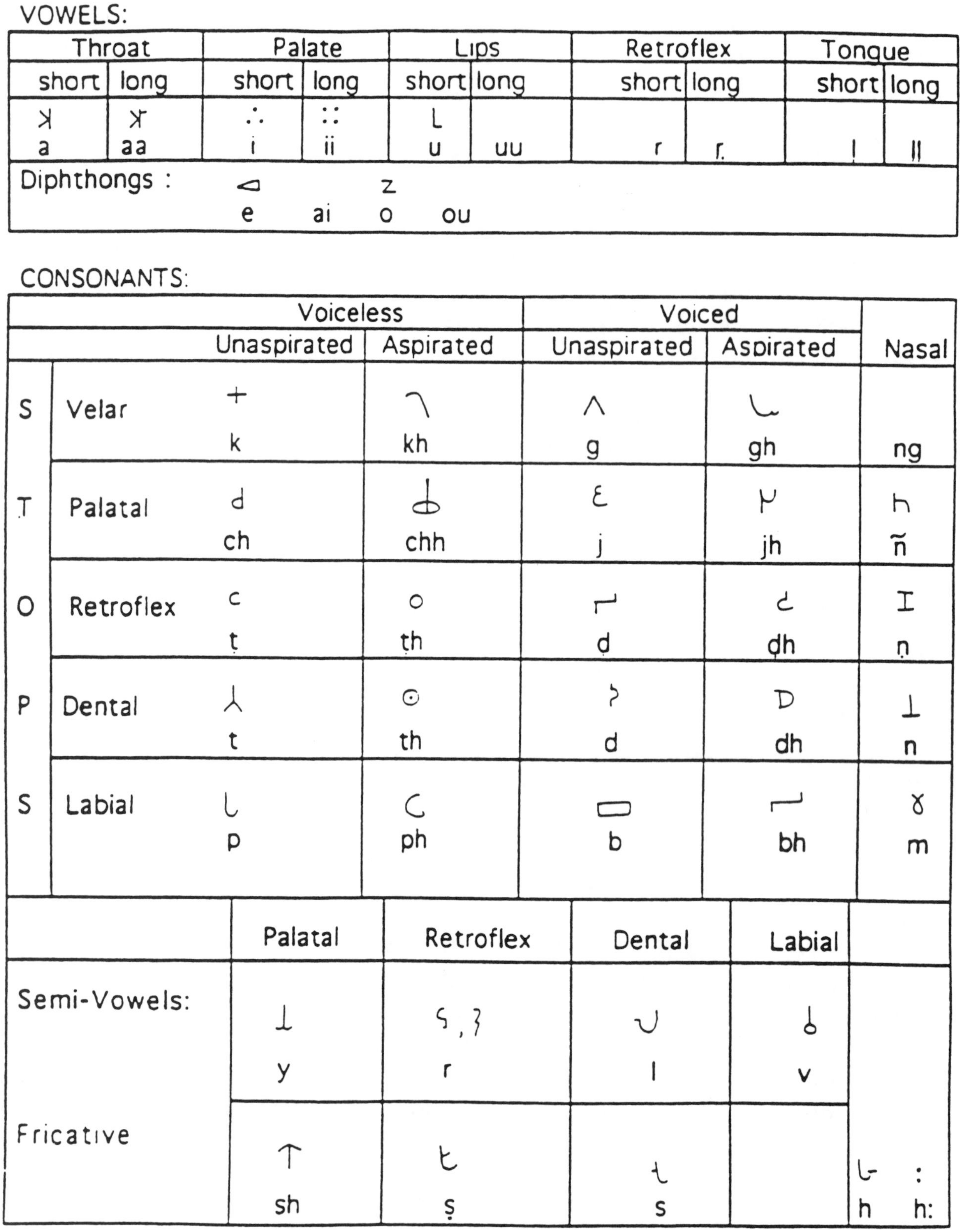

VOWELS:

Throat		Palate		Lips		Retroflex		Tongue	
short	long	short	long	short	long	short	long	short	long
a	aa	i	ii	u	uu	r	r.	l	ll
Diphthongs :	e	ai	o	ou					

CONSONANTS:

		Voiceless		Voiced		
		Unaspirated	Aspirated	Unaspirated	Aspirated	Nasal
S	Velar	k	kh	g	gh	ng
T	Palatal	ch	chh	j	jh	ñ
O	Retroflex	ṭ	ṭh	ḍ	ḍh	ṇ
P	Dental	t	th	d	dh	n
S	Labial	p	ph	b	bh	m

	Palatal	Retroflex	Dental	Labial	
Semi-Vowels:	y	r	l	v	
Fricative	sh	ṣ	s		h h:

Diringer states "perfection in an alphabet implies the accurate rendering of phonemes that is, each sound must be represented by a single constant symbol, and not more than one sound by the same symbol" (v. I, p. 166). Almost all scholars would agree with Diringer. One should also add that all the different sounds of that particular language must be represented by individual signs. By this definition, *Brahmi is probably the only perfect alphabet,* in the world, since it is based on perfect phonetical analysis of a language, the Vedic Sanskrit. Although the analysis by the older phoneticians was by far the major part of the invention of the Brahmi alphabet, the way the consonant letters was used also shows the work of a brilliant phonetician. How to pronounce the consonants? "A vowel with a consonant, or even by itself, forms a syllable," says an ancient Indian phonetician (Allen, 29), and nobody can pronounce anything less than a syllable in any language, for example, only consonants. So the phonetician-script designer recommended pronouncing all the consonants in syllables by using a short vowel sound /a/ just after it, and made the sounds of all the consonants symmetrical. For example, ka, kha, ga, gha, ca, chha, ja, jha, *etc.*

The predecessors of the Phoenicians vocalized their consonants by naming the animals or the objects, aleph, beth, gimmel, daleth, and others, a clumsy way to pronounce the consonants and spell them in a word. Did they know that consonants cannot be pronounced without a vowel? The Greeks avoided the whole problem by borrowing the Phoenician words, meaningless in Greek, alpha, beta, gamma, delta, *etc.*

The popular belief among scholars that the Brahmi alphabet is syllabic cannot be accepted. As we have already seen that the Indian phoneticians achieved perfection in the analysis of the consonants of the Sanskrit language at the deepest phonetic level, so the individual letters used for each of them have to be pure consonants. Furthermore, Sanskrit, having 34 consonant and 14 vowel sounds would have needed 476 (34 x 14) separate syllabic characters to represent the syllables of the language. However, the Brahmi alphabet represents all the phonetic elements of the Sanskrit language with only 48 alphabetic characters. Moreover, all syllabic writing, like the Sumerian, Linear B, Japanese kana, and others, has individual signs for each syllable; but the Brahmi alphabet does not. Brahmi had only one individual sign for each of the 36 consonant sounds. Moreover, to pronounce the consonants individual diacritical marks were developed for each of the vowels; some of them are shown here:

ka kaa ki kii ku kuu ke kai ko

As Coulmas (184) observed, "since vowels are indicated by diacritical marks and are thus clearly distinguished from the consonant part of the basic sign, the script cannot justly be called "syllabic." The individual consonants could not be pronounced, so it was recommended to pronounce with a short /a/ after it. However, when there was no vowel after a consonant, a diacritical mark for no vowel was used. Of course, full vowel signs were always used at the beginning of the word, and whenever their use was required. There was no inherent short /a/ sound after every consonant, as popularly believed. In that case Ka + i (+̄) or Ta + u (人) should have been pronounced as Kai and Tau, respectively. This never happened; they were always pronounced as Ki and Tu. Moreover, if there was a consonant cluster in the writing, the so called 'inherent' vowels inbetween the consonants were never pronounced, proving that the short /a/ is not inherent as Jensen correctly believes (262-263). One may say that the /a/ to pronounce a consonant in the Indian System, is no more adherent than 'eta,' and 'amma' are to beta and gamma in Greek, or 'ee' in bee, cee are in English. *Therefore, we can conclude that the Brahmi is a pure alphabetic system.* Furthermore, the units of consonants attached to the diacritical marks for the vowels made the Brahmi writing linear. However, Brahmi derived scripts are not often so.

THE DATE AND PLACE OF INVENTION OF THE BRAHMI ALPHABET

We first encounter the Brahmi alphabet in large numbers in the edicts of King Ashoka, who ascended the throne in 269 B.C., and lived until 232 B.C. Earlier, a few coins in the fourth century B.C. also showed several signs of the Brahmi alphabet. King Ashoka's capital was Pataliputra, in Magadha, Eastern India. These edicts are almost all over India and Afghanistan, within his empire. Most of them were written in the Brahmi script, except in Northwest India and Afghanistan, where the script was in Brahmi derived Kharosthi. As the Brahmi characters showed considerable variations in shapes in different parts of India, they suggest that the origin was at least a few hundred years old at the time of King Asoka.

We will show that the invention of the Brahmi alphabet belongs to the earlier period of intellectual revolt in the later half of the seventh century B.C. "The age in which true history appears in India," Basham writes, "was one of great intellectual and spiritual ferment,...the age of Buddha (c. 566-486 B.C.), it produced not only philosophers and ascetics, but merchant princes and men of action" (45). He continues, "Only in the time of Buddha, under the great King Bimbisara (ruled 545-490 B.C.), did Magadha begin to show the energy and initiative which were to lead to the setting up of the first great Indian empire" (Ibid, 40). Bimbisara's capital was Rajagriha, southeast of Pataliputra, also near the birthplace of Gautama Siddharta.

Gautama Siddhartha was the name of Buddha before he attained enlightenment. He was born in Kapilabastu, the son of the ruler of a small Kingdom of *Sakyas*, at the border of Nepal and Magadha (Bihar, Eastern India). According to *Lalitavistara*, a legendary poem on the life of Buddha, probably written a few centuries after his death, he was highly proficient in arithmetic and could read and write. Although his literacy cannot be proven from the book, he certainly knew the Brahmi alphabet and the old Indian numerals as we will show, the writing system was available in his childhood near his birthplace. The creator of the Brahmi alphabet was certainly a Brahmin scholar, since he knew the phonetic analysis of the Vedas. He was also highly unorthodox; his writing of the sacred Hindu scriptures, carried orally for centuries by many Brahmin families, would have made them available to everybody, including the non-Brahmins.

King Darius (522-486 B.C.) and his scholars invented a writing system for the Old Persian language in the simplified cuneiform characters of the Akkadians; but the inner phonetic structure was borrowed from the Indians. Diringer (113) says that analysis of this structure disproves the notion of gradual development, and the phonetic structure on which the signs were based reveals a very strong Indian influence. Homel (quoted by Diringer,110) noted that "the underlying alphabet was the same as that which also provided the model of the Indian script." The order of the letters of Old Persian script, is typical of the Brahmi system, vowels first and then consonants in phonetical order, and each consonant was pronounced with a /a/ sound. They had, however, many individual signs for syllables. Brahmi never had individual syllabic signs they are Persian modification. The alphabet with syllabic signs is in this order: a, i, u; Ka, Ku, xa, ga, gu, ch, j, ji, ta, tu, sa, da, di, du, na, nu pa, fa, ba, ma, mi, mu, ya, ra, ru, la, va, vi, sa, sa, za, ha. The Persians also added extra signs for King, country, earth, god and Ahuramazda.

We know that several centuries earlier only the Indians were analyzing the Vedic Sanskrit language phonetically in that fashion. No Brahmin, however, would have taught the phonetical analysis of the Vedas to a non-Brahmin Persian. Therefore, the Persians must have taken it from an Indian script, and the origin of the Brahmi alphabet must have preceded the creation of the Old Persian writing system by King Darius (c. 500 B.C.). The Persians took the phonetic base not from the Brahmi but from its descendant, the Kharosthi alphabet which was used in Afghanistan, adjacent to Persia. The Brahmi system spread from Magadha, in Eastern India through Kharosthi script in Northwest India and Afghanistan, about 2,500 miles away to Persia. This probably accounted for about 100 to 150 years, thus placing the lower limit of the origin of the Brahmi alphabet around 650 to 600 B.C. The systematic phonetic analysis of the *Vedas* probably was not done before the eighth century B.C. Furthermore, the writing for the sacred Vedas, a sacrilegious act, could have been accomplished only when there was an intellectual revolt against the orthodox Brahminism. In the light of all these factors the Brahmi script was probably created in the later half of the seventh century B.C. The greatness of the Brahmi alphabetic system is not its antiquity but in originality and perfection.

The location of the origin of the Brahmi alphabet was almost certainly in the Magadha, between Eastern Nepal and Northern Bengal, the most prosperous area of India during that period. This was the area where the intellectual revolt against the orthodox Brahmanism started, and later culminated in the revolutionary teaching of Buddha, and his contemporary Mahavira, and others. This was before the time of King Bimbisara (who ruled 545-490 B.C.). So the creator of the Brahmi alphabetic signs most probably lived in the vicinity of Rajagriha, later the capital city of King Bimbisara in Magadha. Prince Siddhartha's (Buddha) birthplace was only 175 miles from Rajagriha. When the Brahmi alphabet was invented, in the later part of the seventh century B.C., the nearest script available was the cuneiform of the Akkadians, almost 3,000 miles away. The other was the Chinese script, but the Indian Buddhist preachers first started going to China in the first century A.D. Because of mass deportations by the Akkadian king the Aramaic people were scattered throughout his empire, the Aramaic script started spreading to Persia. This was after the time of the invention of the Persian script by King Darius (c. 500 B.C.); therefore, it was after the spread of Brahmi derived Kharosthi script to Persia.

This was the time of the Akkadian King Ashurbanipal (668-627 B.C.) or just after it, and they used the cuneiform characters for their language. The Persian King Darius created the Old Persian writing, entirely from the Indian phonetic base and the cuneiform characters, and there was no influence of the Aramaic script before or during this period in Persia.

The following map shows the area of the origin of the Brahmi alphabet, in the Magadha, centering in the city of Rajagriha, and near the birthplace of Buddha in Kapilabastu. It also shows the spread of the Brahmi system through Kharosthi to the Old Persian writing of King Darius.

Fig. 6. SPREAD OF THE PHONETICAL BASE OF BRAHMI TO OLD PERSIAN

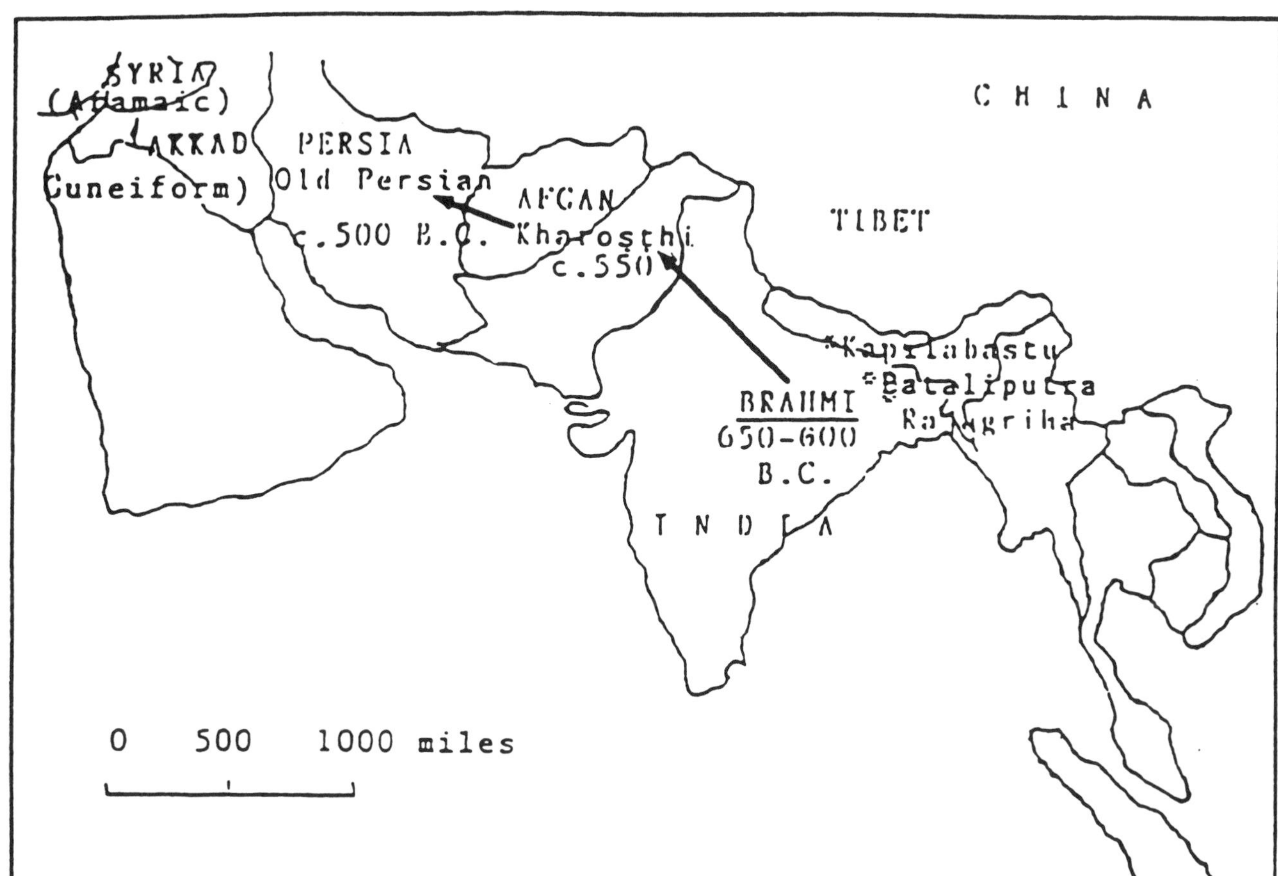

At present there are numerous theories on the origin of the Brahmi alphabet. Most Indian scholars think that the Brahmi descended from the writing system of the Harappan civilization (Indus valley), which lasted from approximately 2,500 to around 1,700 B.C. This civilization is the third oldest original one, after the Sumerian and the Egyptian. Harappan civilization spread along the Indus River valley, now in Pakistan, and to Gujarat, Western India, most extensive in area of all the original major civilizations. The major towns were well planned, almost in identical design, with parallel streets running north to south and, crossing them at right angles, east to west. One of the outstanding feature was a covered drainage system unequaled until the 19th century European cities. The Harappans produced beautiful, realistic figures of dancer, priest, and various animals. The early Indians invented a writing system of about 400 individual characters, the number suggest syllabic writing. The language is controvertial, Dravidian or Sanskrit. Scholars differ interpreting the sounds and the meaning of the characters, some are shown below:

The characters are clearly of pictographic origin, different animals, particularly, fish, man in various postures and other signs; in contrast, all Brahmi letters are geometrical. Some of the Harappan pictograms carrying diacritical marks on the main characters reminding one of marks on the Brahmi characters for vowel differentiation. The Aryan invasion of India probably did not start before 1,500 B.C. Thus the influence on the Brahmi based on a few diacritical marks after a thousand years makes this theory untenable. Until the language, sounds and the meanings are uncontrovertially deciphered the origin of the Brahmi from the Harappan writing is unacceptable. Most western scholars believe that the Brahmi alphabet is derived from a Semitic script, the old North Semitic (old Phoenician) or the Aramaic. Jensen (365) gives his views as follows:

> Two inscriptions from the Iranian border-area, namely 1. The Taxila inscription in the Aramaic language and script; 2. The stone at Puli-i-Darunta, east of Kabul, also in Aramaic script, though the language is partly Aramaic and partly east Iranian. We know after all, that the first Seleucid rulers, whose sphere of influence extended, as is well known, from Syria across Persia and as far as the borders of India (312-240 B.C.) used the Aramaic language and script alongside the Greek as the language of administration; it seems very natural to assume that the chancellary of the North-Indian Maurya empire (318-185) took over the Aramaic script from there.

There are several major flaws in this theory. First, we have already established that this period was at least three centuries later than the origin of the Brahmi alphabet. This alone invalidates Jensen's theory. Second, the Aramaic writing system had no influence in Persia before or during the reign of King Darius, which we have already shown. So when the Brahmi alphabet was created, the influence of Aramaic did not even spread to Persia. Third, historically, the non-phonetic structure of the Semitic system could never be changed to the phonetic structure on which the Brahmi letters were based. Most important point is that only *one* of the 48 letters of Brahmi matches one Aramaic character with the same sound /g/ in Jensen's table, Fig. 343, p. 367.

Comparison between the Old Phoenician and the Brahmi characters, according to Gelb; part of (Fig.77, p.142), is as follows: Fig. 7.

Phonetic Value	d	z	l	n	'	p	q	w	t
Semitic Signs	⊿	I	L	ɣ	o	7	ϙ	⩡	+
Brahmi Signs	>	I	L	ɗ	o	7	ȸ	ᒪ	+
Phonetic Value	e	n	u	d	th	kh	ch	gh	k

Gelb compares the 22 Old Phoenician signs with the Brahmi characters, and found that nine of the signs are similar, but none of them had the same sound. Therefore, Gelb (187) concludes, "The forms of the individual signs of Brahmi writing show no clear relationship with any other system, and were most probably freely invented."

Fig.8. COMPARISON BETWEEN ARAMAIC AND BRAHMI ALPHABETS

SOUNDS	.	B	G	D	E	W	Zayin	E	T	Y	K
Aramaic	F, x	ﻯ	∧	4	╥	7	Z	H			7, ˥
Brahmi	⅄	▭	∧	⊃	Ⴑ	⊥̇		⊿		⊥	+
SOUNDS	L	M	N	S	'Ain	P	Sade	Q	R	S	T
Aramaic	Ն	ⁿ˥	ʕ	3, ვ		?	℞	P	7	v, v	+
Brahmi	ᒍ	γ	⊥	⅄		U	Ⴒ		ʃ	T	C

All evidence confirms that no Semitic or any other script, including Aramaic, had any influence on either the phonetic base or the signs of the Brahmi alphabet. All ancient scripts, except the Egyptian hieroglyphs, were like children's scribbles and the easiest aspect of the writing systems.

It is most important in finding the origin of an alphabet to look at the *order of the letters* in the alphabet, which is based on the phonetical analysis of that particular language.

Fig.9. THE ORDER OF LETTERS IN TWO DIFFERENT ALPHABETIC SYSTEMS

PHOENICIAN-GREEK	INDIAN BRAHMI
Vowels and Consonants mixed Non-phonetic Arrangement	Vowels and cosonants separated Phonetic arrangement
A, b,c,d, E, f,g,h, I, j,k,l,m, n, O, p,q,r,s,t, U, v,w,x,y,z	A, Ā, I, Ī, U, Ū, Ṛ, Ḷ, E, AI, O, OU k, kh, g, gh, ṅ : c, ch, j, jh, ñ ṭ, ṭh, ḍ, ḍh, ṇ : t, th, d, dh, n p, ph, b, bh, m : y,r,l,v,ś,s,ṣ,h

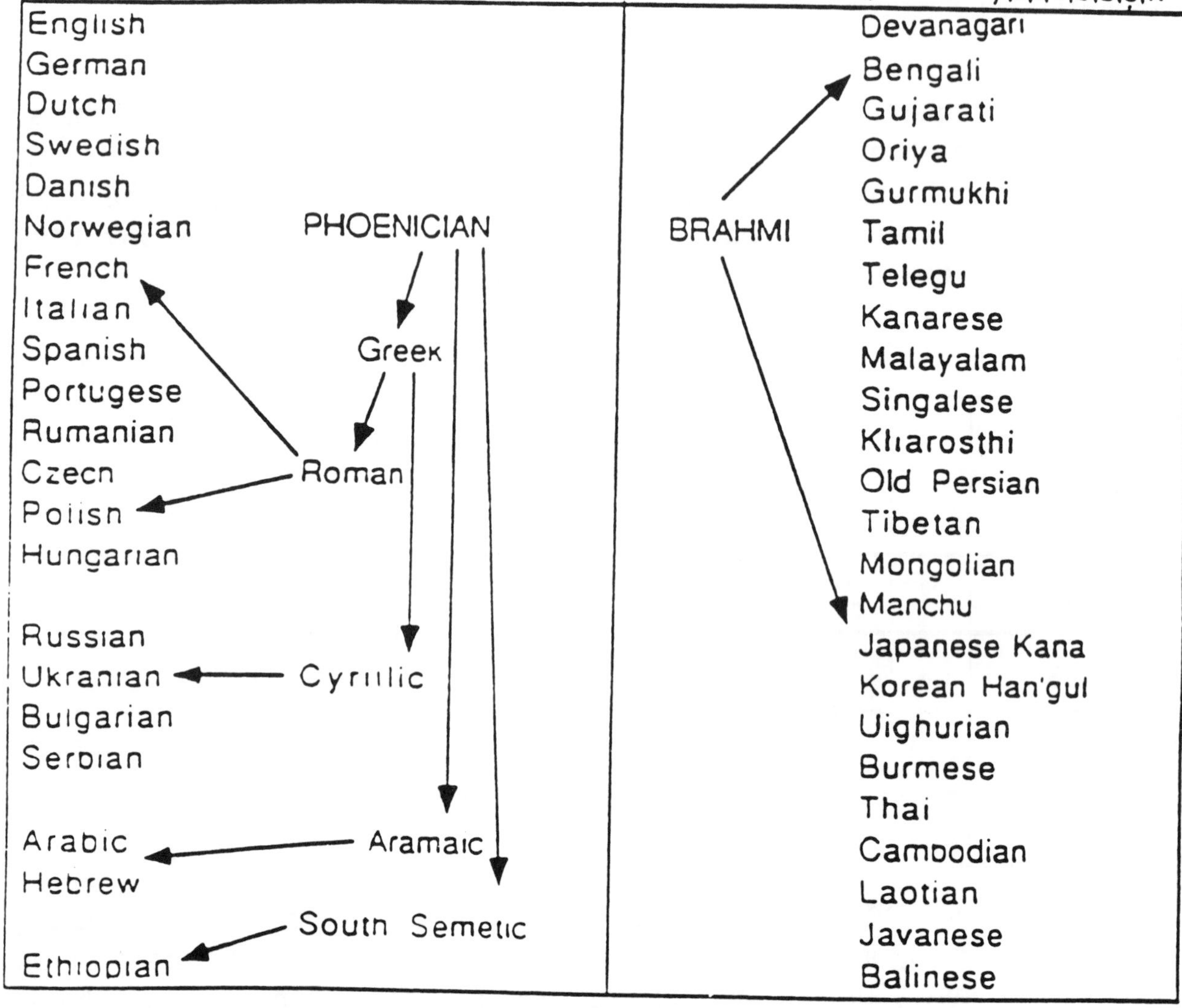

The separation of the vowels and the consonants in the order of the letters is the hallmark of the Indian system, whereas mixed vowel and consonant signs are the characteristics of the Phoenician-Greek system.

This difference is maintained, *without a single exception,* in all the hundreds of languages written in each of these two alphabetic systems. Once an orthography is placed in the Brahmi system by this method, one also finds that the vowels and the consonants are organized in a phonetic arrangement as the borrowers adjust it to their language. Further confirmation is always available that Buddhism carried the alphabet to Central, North, and Northeast Asia, and Hinduism did the same to all the countries of South and Southeast Asia. All other standard methods of comparison will also confirm the origin: for example, similarities in the characters with the corresponding sounds, pronunciation of the consonants with a short /a/, left to right direction of writing, trade relations, tradition, and others. This is equally true for all the languages using the Phoenician-Greek system which carried over all their totally different characteristics from the Brahmi system.

Any fundamental change in the order of the alphabet is unknown in the history of borrowing. The phonetic structure as well as the signs between these two alphabetic systems are fundamentally so different that they rule out any mutual influence or common origin. When we learn an alphabet from parents or teachers, we always learn the old fixed order of the letters. Similarly, when an unwritten language adapts an alphabetic system, the order of the letters is always maintained with only minor modifications to fit the sounds of the language. Also, in some civilizations the letters are used as numbers where the continued use of the same order is essential. *Therefore, we can conclude that the phonetic structure, and the characters of the Brahmi alphabet were independently invented in Magadha in the latter part of the seventh century B.C.*

The importance of the phonetic base was expressed by Professor Diringer: (1960, p. 38).

> The great achievement in the creation of the alphabet was not the invention of signs - ample evidence can be adduced for the invention of alphabet by schoolchildren who already know their ABC - but the inner working principle. This in its simplicity was the production of a system in which each sound was represented by one sign. The inventor of this system must, indeed, have been a very fine phonetician. For the achievement, simple as it now seems to us, the inventor is to be ranked among the greatest benefactors of mankind.

This remark was meant for the inventor of the Old Semitic consonantal alphabet. However, these words are far more applicable to the creation of the Brahmi alphabet. As regards the signs of the alphabet, Gelb (144) says, "In practice simple forms of straight lines, triangles, squares, circles are usually chosen,...and the number of such forms is limited....only about sixty individual signs were found in the area surrounding the Mediterranean basin by Petrie."

Although we have given enough evidence for two origins of the alphabets, we will discuss why the present theories of the origin of the Brahmi alphabet are not correct. No evidence has been found to support the theory of pictographic origin of the Brahmi alphabet. It is interesting to note that even those scholars who think that the Brahmi alphabet is borrowed from a Semitic source are uncomfortable with the idea. Diringer (262) believes that the Brahmi was derived from the Aramaic script. However, he says, "It was probably mainly the *idea* of alphabetic writing which was accepted...they were the inventors of this essentially national alphabet, regardless of the problem concerning the original source of the idea. The fully developed Brahmi system, an outcome of the remarkable philological and phonological precision wherein the early Indians surpassed all ancient peoples." Jensen says that the Brahmi is "unmistakably the work of Brahmins skilled in philology. (370)." He also says, "an Indian trader brought the script from the Semitic." This would be impossible since an Indian trader, a Vaishya by caste, would have no knowledge of the Vedic phonetics. If he borrowed from any of the Semitic writing system, he would have taken the Semitic characters with the corresponding Semitic names and the order of letters. All borrowers of alphabetic writing follow this rule. Gelb says that "The form of individual signs of the Brahmi writing shows no clear relationship with any other system, and was most probably freely invented" (187). However, he believes that the "Indic system.... structurally, if not formally....is derived from a Semitic prototype" (150). I have already shown that the structure (phonetic) of Brahmi alphabet is totally different from that of the Semitic-Greek system. Coulmas (185) writes: "Whatever form of Semitic writing was introduced into India in the eighth or seventh century B.C. was thoroughly nativized and recreated - that is consciously redesigned along segmental phonemic lines - by the ancient Indians." He continues, "Until corroborated by hard archeological evidence, this explanation of the origin of Indic writing, too, can be regarded only as a plausible hypothesis." Sampson (77) comments on the origin of the alphabet that: "Most, and probably all, alphabetic script derive from a single ancestor: the Semitic alphabet, created sometime in the -2nd millennium. (The possible exceptions are the Indian family of alphabets)." DeFrancis (274, notes, 2) suggests on the Indian writing system, "perhaps we have here an indigenous development that might be considered a second invention of phonemic writing." *Therefore, the conclusion is that there are two origins of all writng systems and alphabets used today.*

Sanskrit was a spoken language for about 1,000 years. However, by the time the great grammarian Panini standardized the classical Sanskrit about 2,500 years ago, the general population spoke in various forms of Prakrit, all derived from the Sanskrit. The Prakrit language had a much simpler grammar and sound system. It is interesting to note that most of the earlier use of the Brahmi alphabet, preserved in epigraphy, was not for Sanskrit but for its descendants. Buddha preached probably in Magadhi (Basham, 391), the spoken language of his time, in the northeastern part of India. However, the most important early scriptures of Buddhism were written in Pali, also derived from Sanskrit, and used the Brahmi alphabet.

King Ashoka, born a Hindu, converted himself to Buddhism in remorse after he saw that his powerful army had killed over a 100,000 soldiers of the Kalinga kingdom. It was unique in history that a victorious King abandoned war, and preached and practiced peace, internally and with other kingdoms. In King Asoka's words, which are engraved on a rock:

> When the King....after eight years of war Kalinga was conquered, 150,000 people were taken captive, 100,000 were killed, and many more died....That the beloved of the gods [as King Asoka called himself] began to follow righteousness. When an unconqured country is conquered, people are killed, they die, or are made captive. That the beloved of the gods find very pitiful and grievous....he is not only compassionate but also powerful, and he tells them to repent. The beloved of the gods desire self-control, justice and happiness for all beings....the greatest of of all victories is the victory of righteousness (Basham, 53).

Almost all the edicts of King Asoka were in the Prakrit language, with local variations throughout his empire in India and Afghanistan. During the reign of King Ashoka a second type of script was used in the Northwest region of his empire, now in Afghanistan and adjacent part of Pakistan; it was known as Kharoṣṭhi. Most scholars think that the Kharoṣṭhi script was derived from the Aramaic mainly because it was written from right to left and a few characters are similar. When Kharosthi originated, before King Darius, the Aramaic alphabet did not spread to Persia. The phonetic base of Kharosthi is identical to Brahmi, vowels separated from consonants and arranged in phonetical order. Only three characters out of 37 in Kharoṣṭhi script have similar letters and sounds matching the Aramaic, this is probably a coincidence. It is probable that the creator of Kharoṣṭhi heard about, or saw the Aramaic characters. However, we do not see any significant influence of the Aramaic writing system on the phonetic base of or the signs of Kharoṣṭhi.

Since the Kharoṣṭhi lacks two Vedic vowel characters (ṛ and ḷ), it is much more cursive, and it was used over a 1,000 miles away from Magadha; we can conclude therefore, that the Kharoṣṭhi was borrowed from the Brahmi. It is interesting that only three kharoṣṭhi characters are similar to Brahmi but none of them has matching sound. Why did anyone design an alphabet with the phonetic base of the Brahmi but in a different script for the same Prakrit language? Brahmi was more than adequate for Prakrit. This is like writing the same language in the same alphabetic system but in different scripts, similar to the writing of the Serbo-Croatian language by the Serbians in the Cyrillic alphabet introduced by the Greek Orthodox Church; and the Croatians writing in the Roman alphabet brought by the Roman Catholic Church. Similarly, the Hindustani language is written in Devanagari script by the Hindus, but the Muslims use the Arabic alphabet. Was the designer of the Kharoṣṭhi script a Brahmin who learned the phonetical analysis of the Sanskrit, and later was converted to Buddhism, and wanted to avoid the script of the Brahmins? Why did the orthodox Brahmins name it Kharoṣṭhi (meaning donkey's lips), a derogatory term? Readers may attempt to guess the answers.

From the Brahmi alphabet developed the phonetic base and the signs of all the scripts of India, Tibet, Sri Lanka and all the Southeast Asian countries to the Philippines. Some of the countries took the phonetic base and a few or no signs of the Brahmi, for example, Central and Northern Asia, Western and Northern China. The Japanese kana system, the Korean Han'gul, the Mongolian, and the Manchurian also are based on the phonetic system of the Brahmi alphabet. See the map on the front-cover.

IV. LANGUAGES AND SCRIPTS OF INDIA

India is really a continent, and has a population of about 940 million, compared to all of Europe which contains 755 million people. Twelve languages are each spoken by over ten million Indians. Eight of these are descendants of the Sanskrit language: (in millions) Hindi (393), Bengali (74 in India and 127 in Bangladesh), Marathi (70), Urdu (48 in India and 11 in Pakistan), Gujarati (37), Punjabi (27 in India and 68 in Pakistan), Oriya (32), and Assamese (15). The four other major languages in South India classified as Dravidian languages, are Telegu (76), Tamil (63), Kannada (38), and Malayalam (37) (estimated from Census,1991). Together, the twelve major languages are the mother tongues of 93% of Indians. The majority of the rest usually speak at least one of the major languages.

Europe has fifteen languages, used as mother tongue by over ten million people, 88% of the population: Russian (169), German (86), English (59), French (57), Italian (55), Polish (38), Ukrainian (36), Spanish (29), Dutch (20), Romanian (20), Serbo-Croat (15), Greek (10), Portuguese (10), and Czech (10). All of them are Indo-European languages. Hungarian (10) is a Finno-Ugric language. So, the linguistic richness of Europe and India is comparable.

India has nine major scripts: Devanagari (for Hindi, Marathi, Nepali), Bengali (also Assamese and Manipuri), Telegu-Kanarese, Tamil, Malayalam, Gujarati, oriya, Gurmukhi (Punjabi), all derived from the Brahmi; only Urdu is written in modified Arabic script. Europe has three scripts: Roman, Cyrillic, and Greek. Diversity in languages or scripts is not the problem of India. Switzerland, by far per capita the richest country in the world, not involved in wars for centuries, political power resides in 26 cantons, recognizes four official languages. Although German is the mother tongue of more than 70% of the Swiss population it is not forced on others.

Ancient Indians built a tradition of intellectually analyzing every aspect of their lives and their surroundings. This is exemplified in Buddha's eight paths of ethics, Sankara's monoism (the total unity of all existence, not controlled by an outsider, for example, God), Sankhya's dualistic atheism, Kanada's atomism, Kautilya political economy, Bharata and Nandikesvara's analysis of dance, music, and drama, Vatsayana's study of hedonistic life including sex, Susruta's surgery, Caraka's medicine, chess, the most intellectual, and polo, most regal of all games as well as many other accomplishments. After the repeated devastation by the Islamic hordes, India lost its intellectual tradition. Furthermore, India missed the European Renaissance, part of the Industrial, and the 20th century technological Revolution. After India became independent from the British rule in 1947, for five decades it followed unreal economic, foreign, and military policies leading to slow economic growth. India has a large number of skilled people, large middlle class in a partially free economy. One hopes that Indian leaders decides to stop wasting money in the Armed Forces instead invest in agriculture,Industry, communication etc.

Over 40% of Indians speak Hindi, which is the national language, and covers six states and the capital New Delhi. The entire area is called the Hindi belt. About 9% of the population of the Hindi belt uses Urdu as their mother tongue. Each of the other ten major language speakers have their own state, situated east, south and west of the Hindi belt. The standard Hindi (Khariboli), Urdu, and Hindustani languages are based on the dialect of the Delhi-Meerat area. They have the same grammar and frequently used vocabulary. The Hindustani language, the *lingua franca* of North India, is written either in Devanagari or in Arabic script. Mahatma Gandhi was a great supporter of Hindustani, and highly entertaining movies from Bombay popularized the language, and continue to do so. However, only a few are seriously interested in this compromised language for serious literature, and its future is in doubt. For the last hundred years Hindi writers have used increasing numbers of Sanskrit words, and used the Devanagari alphabet, whereas Urdu has adapted much Arabic and Persian vocabulary, and is written in modified Arabic script. Now they are gradually becoming two different languages, and unlike the Serbo-Croatian language with two scripts, Cyrillic and Roman. Urdu means "camp," and the language originated around the Dehli area. When the Muslim invaders, living in camps, had to communicate with the local Hindus, they used the mixed language. Urdu flourished under the patronage of the Muslim rulers and, later, the British, at the expense of Hindi. Even in the first three decades of the 20th century most well educated Hindus, Muslims, and Sikhs in the Hindi belt and Punjab used Urdu. As the Hindus and Sikhs are gradually abandoning Urdu, in the next generation almost all Urdu speakers will be Muslims. However, over a third of Muslims live outside the Hindi belt, and their mother tongues and scripts are the same as the Hindus, for example, Bengali, Malayalam, Telegu, and others.

Things changed in the1920s with the nationalist movement, and in the 1930s when the leading Urdu novelist Prem Chand changed his works from Urdu to Hindi. About the same time a group of poets, influenced by Bengali literature, called themselves the "Chayabadis" first started writing imaginative poems in Hindi. Surprisingly, imaginative literature in standard Hindi (Khariboli) has a short history of only over a hundred years, compared to hundreds and thousands of years for all other major Indian languages. Poetry in the Hindi belt used to be written in Brajabhasa, Maithili, Awadhi, Rajathani, and others. These languages and dialects are extensively used today in their own regions, but the medium of instruction at schools is standard Hindi. Bengali has the richest modern literature and Tamil has the longest literary tradition of two thousand years. Sanskrit dominates all the languages of India, and is a continuing source of ideas and vocabulary.

English is the mother tongue of only 330,000 Indians, and is used by more than 48 million people. In 1947 English was temporarily selected as one of the two national languages until 1965, after which only Hindi would have continued as the national language. However, it seems that India cannot live without English. The stigma of its being the foreign rulers' language long gone, English in India is flourishing as never before. There are more students in English medium schools, almost half of the books (titles) are published in English compared to 9% in Hindi, 7% in Bengali (excluding Bangladesh), 6% in Marathi. As in the past, imaginative literature is predominantly written in Indian languages, and scientific books and journals in English; "Even in New Delhi, the center of Hindi area, indicates higher use of English in the utilitarian domain, and mother tongue in affective domain" (Kachru,143). Sridhar (145), in a study of 299 students and 88 employees in Karnataka, asked which language they would choose if a choice were available: 68% preferred English, 27% their mother tongue, and 5% Hindi/Urdu. India has lost most of its enquiring tradition of ancient times, and because of the low economic level, none of the linguistic areas, including Hindi, has enough high quality research workers to produce up-to-date scientific journals and books at a reasonable standard. This would be only possible if they were nationally accessible; thus most scientific journals are published in English.

Illiteracy is a major problem in India. The 1991 census shows that literacy rate is 52%. However, one should realize that most of the Indian illiterates have not had any chance to go to school or to continue education because of poverty, and not because of mental inadequacy. Anyone who has observed them know that Indian voters, literate or illiterate, though highly emotional, are fairly informed and decisive. Mental arithmetical calculation is often good among many illiterates. Literacy is unevenly distributed in India. The four populous states in the Hindi belt, U.P., Bihar, M.P., and Rajasthan, with 36% of India's population, have an average literacy rate of 40%, whereas the states surrounding them have achieved the literac y rate of 60% on the average. The tribal Mizos, in the east, bordering Burma, have 81% literacy, and the major Dravidian language speaking Malayalees, in Kerala in South India, have always led the country in mass education; they are 90% literate.

Some writers have proposed to use the Davanagari Alphabet for all the languages in India. This would certainly drop the literacy rate of the highly literate states of India, an effort achieved over many decades at great human and financial expenses. Most of the advocates fail to understand that just learning the alphabet is the essential first step but a small part of literacy. To read and understand a few pages in any new script requires a recognition of the patterns of the words and phrases, which takes almost a year or more for an average person. Those who individually spell and decipher many words are still semiliterates, for they cannot understand even the content of the text. To adapt the Roman script for the Indian languages would be even worse as it would involve all of India. Furthermore, the number of Roman letters, particularly for the vowels, are inadequate for most Indian languages.

There are at least 40 scripts in India, and about 35 outside India, used for hundreds of languages, developed from the Brahmi alphabet. Several of them are for major languages and are used extensively in many parts of Asia, while others are minor or extinct. The Brahmi derived alphabets, however, over the centuries and millenia deteriorated both in symbols and their use for other languages. None could preserve the perfection of the Brahmi alphabet in phonetical use or the simplicity of the signs. The script became increasingly cursive, and many ligatures developed to the point that the individual letters were often not identifiable. Some of the letters in Brahmi were not needed for the borrowed languages, but their use continued. On the other hand, the borrowers often did not design new signs for new sounds in their languages.

The shapes of the characters have gradually changed through the Kushana dynasty around the first century A.D., to the prosperous Gupta Dynasty (fourth to sixth century A.D.) when many of the characters retained some similarity to the Brahmi script. This script was called Gupta script. Opinions of scholars differ on the subsequent growth of the Gupta script. R.D. Banerjee (24 ff) mentioned four varieties: the Western, Eastern, Southern, and the Central Asian. Bühler (quoted by Jensen, 375) further distinguishes six basic types in Northern India: the Acute Angled Siddhamatṛka, Nagari, Sarada, proto-Bengali, Nepalese hook type, and the arrowhead type. Chakravarti, in his thoroughly researched monogram on the origin of the Bengali alphabet (p.360) thinks that the eastern variety of the Gupta script was already present before the Guptas, and it was displaced by the western variety before 588 A.D. In the seventh century, the western variety of North Indian alphabet branched into western and the eastern varieties. The western branch, the acute angled *Siddhamatṛka*, progressed to the Nagari alphabet by the eighth century, whereas the eastern branch developed towards the proto-Bengali alphabet by the tenth century. From this the Bengali characters developed by the end of eleventh and the beginning of the twelfth century (Ibid).

The Devanagari script is used for Hindi and the languages and dialects of the Hindi belt, Marathi, Nepalese, and several minor languages. The Devanagari alphabet covers about 420 million people, the third largest system of alphabets after the Roman and the Arabic. There is a mistaken belief among most scholars that the Devanagari scripts is the alphabet for Sanskrit language; often this leads to wrong conclusions. As we have already seen, only the Brahmi alphabet was created for the Sanskrit; Devanagari developed about 1,500 years later from the Brahmi, and unable to keep the perfection of the Brahmi alphabet. It was only about a hundred years ago that most of the universities of India decided to print all Sanskrit books published by them in Devanagari characters, and books in the Pali language in Roman alphabet. Sanskrit was almost always written, for well over 2,000 years, in the local scripts of their time. Even in the last hundred years majority of Sanskrit books, mostly on the Hindu religion, have been written with translations (bilingual) in different Indian languages in local scripts.

Fig. 10. DEVANAGARI SCRIPT

Vowels	अ a	आ aa	इ i	ई ii	उ u	ऊ uu	ऋ ṛ	ए e	ऐ ei	ओ o	औ ou
Consonants	क k	ख kh	ग g	घ gh	ङ ñg	च c	छ ch	ज j	झ jh	ञ ñ	
	ट ṭ	ठ ṭh	ड ḍ	ढ ḍh	ण ṇ	त t	थ th	द d	ध dh	न n	
	प p	फ ph	ब b	भ bh	म m	य y	र r	ल l	व v		
				श š	ष ś	स s	ह h				

BENGALI ALPHABET

The Bengali alphabet is used for the Bengali, Assamese, Manipuri, and various other smaller groups of languages in Eastern India and Bangladesh comprising about 200 million people. This is the fifth most commonly used alphabet, after the Roman, Arabic, Devanagari, and Cyrillic.

Fig.11. BENGALI SCRIPT

Vowels:	অ a	আ aa	ই i	ঈ ii	উ u	ঊ uu	ঋ ṛ	এ e	ঐ ai	ও o	ঔ au
Consonants:		ক k	খ kh	গ g	ঘ gh	ঙ n	চ c	ছ ch	জ j	ঝ jh	ঞ ñ
		ট ṭ	ঠ ṭh	ড ḍ	ঢ ḍh	ণ ṇ	ত t	থ th	দ d	ধ dh	ন n
		প p	ফ ph	ব b	ভ bh	ম m	য় y	র r	ল l	ব v	
		শ ś	ষ ṣh	স s	হ h						

To a significant extent, Bengali written form has deviated from the standard spoken language. Rabindranath Tagore, the Noble Prize winner in literature in 1913, wrote that we write in Sanskrit and read the same in Bengali (12). Sir George Grierson, the director of the linguistic survey of India, said that the Bengalees write as in Latin and read them like Italian. This is undoubtedly true with almost all the *tatsama* words, the Sanskrit words written in Sanskrit spelling in the Bengali script but pronounced in the Bengali way. These words were borrowed directly from the Sanskrit in the course of last several centuries; 44% of Bengali words are in this group (Chatterjee, v. I, 218). The other source of Bengali vocabulary is the *tatbhava* words spelled and pronounced in the Bengali way, although all of these words were ultimately derived from the Sanskrit, changed through the various stages of Prakit, Apabhramsa, and eastern Magadhan. Chatterjee (Ibid) calculated the percentage of this group of words as 51.45%. Tagore (12) thought that this traditional division is artificial, as hardly any Sanskrit word in Bengali is pronounced in correct Sanskrit sound. The number of foreign words, mostly English and Persian-Arabic, are 4.55% in Bengali. During the last 50 years, however, the number of English words have increased by several thousands, but no statistics are available.

Whatever the source of these words, they are almost always pronounced in the standard Bengali way. For example, there are only seven vowels in the Bengali language, front i, e, a, middle a , and back u, o, ae. In the Bengali alphabet, however, following the Sankrit orthography, there are twelve signs for vowels, including separate signs for short and long vowels. Tagore denies any existence of long vowels in the Bengali language except one /kii/ meaning *what*? Thus he prefers to use the short vowel signs only. There are three sibilant phonemes in Sanskrit with three different letters, dental /s/, palatal/sh/, and retroflex /ṣ/. In Bengali orthography all these three letters are used exactly as in Sanskrit. But all educated Bengalee always pronounce any sibilant as /sh/, except before the dentals /t/, /th/, /n/, as well as /r/, and /l/, where dental /s/ is automatically pronounced even without any knowledge of the rule.

In 1936 under the auspices of the University of Calcutta a committee for Bengali spelling reform was organized with all the leading scholars. They agreed on 21 rules to change Bengali spelling, but failed to agree on some major changes, for example, abolition of the long vowels, as well as ṛ and ḷ vowel signs, as they do not exist in the language. In consonants, the velar and palatal 'n' signs are not needed, and to use the sibilant sounds in Bengali characters in Bengali way. Tagore also suggested the use the character 'e' with little modification for the vowel sound /ae/, like 'a' in the English cat, for the frequently used Bengali vowel sound which was not present in Sanskrit. Tagore wanted the alphabet to follow faithfully the Bengali sounds rather than the Sanskrit. Unfortunately, only a few of his ideas were adapted. Bengali orthography is still etymological rather than phonetic. However, as Sanskrit is virtually the only source of Bengali words, the problem is much less than in English spelling; and as there are only a few silent letters in Bengali words, it is simpler than the French.

One of the best examples of strong emotional attachment to one's language and script was the revolt of the Bengali speaking Eastern Pakistanis in 1971. The Western Pakistanis tried to impose Urdu language on the Bengalees and replace the Bengali script by the Arabic. This was one of the major reason for the division of the country into two different Islamic nations, Bangladesh and Pakistan in 1971. Even one of the most brutal genocide in this century by the Pakistani army, killing over two million unarmed Bengalees, systematically eradicating the educated class, raping over 200,000 women, could not stop the division of the country into two parts. Here we see that the mother tongue and the script have more emotional attachment than the ties of the Islamic religion.

Bengali script is also a gradually deteriorated result of the Brahmi alphabet. There are many clumsy consonant cluster signs where it is impossible to recognize the two or occasionally three letters, and sometimes for two or even three consonants, an individual sign was designed. All proposals by scholars to improve the script failed. Fortunately, Suresh Majumdar, the proprietor of The *Ananda Bazar Patrika*, the daily newspaper with the largest circulation from one center in India, decided to use the front upper part of the consonant signs as the first character, followed by the full form of the second letter in a conjoint character. The vowel signs were also made linear. Because of these changes, typing and printing is much easier, and more economical, and the total number of characters or the portion needed for printing, are less than150 (Bandyapadyay, 376).

Bengali is the mother tongue of over 200 million people, the sixth largest group after the Mandarin Chinese, English, Hindi, Spanish and the Arabic. Bengali has the misfortune of being divided between two countries, India and Bangladesh. Since the 16th century the spoken language of the Nawadwip area, just over a hundred miles north of Calcutta, became the standard Bengali in both the spoken and written form. Undoubtedly, the influence of the religious leader Sri Chaitanya of Nawadwip on most aspects of Bengali culture was the major factor. None of the many dialects are used in writing.

Bengali also has a high and a low form of writing (diglossia). Iswar C. Vidyasagar's (1818-1891) writing became the standard for the "chaste" Bengali language this included the verbs in the 16th century form and included many Sanskrit words. The first novel written entirely in colloquial language was *Alaler Ghare Dulal* (1858) which depicted the comical side of the new rich. Since the second decade of this century, the difference between the high chaste language and the colloquial has significantly narrowed. Tagore mentioned that the difference is only in the verbs (9). For example, *bolite* or *bolte* (to speak) are in chaste and colloquial forms respectively. Over the last few decades, the colloquial Bengali speech and its written form have absorbed a large number of Sanskrit words from the high form, and a significant number of English words. There is no prestige attached to the chaste Bengali now, which is not spoken but is still written. The later period of Tagore's writing was marked mostly by use of the colloquial language. Proper usage prohibits mixing the two forms. Only Jibanananda Das (1899-1955), the greatest poet since Tagore, deliberately mixed them.

From the Proto-Bengali script developed the Oriya characters. The striking feature is the rounded instead of straight lines, as a metal stylet would cut palm leaf. In the North the Sarada script was used for Kashmiri, now mostly written in the Arabic script. In Western India the Gujarati script looks like other North Indian scripts except for its abandonment of the unnecessary line above the characters, which improved its appearance. The Sikhs in the Punjab have used the Gurmukhi script for the Punjabi language since the sixteenth century, and their scripture, *Guru Granth* is documented in this script. The characters are somewhat similar to Devanagari.

The Pali script developed from the Brahmi for writing Buddhist literature in Pali and Prakrit languages, and several Southeast Asian scripts developed from it. From the southern branch of the Gupta the Grantha script developed as early as the fifth to seventh centuries, the Sanskrit in South India used to be written in this script. The Tamil language, at an early period, used to be written in Grantha script, but since the eighth century it has been written in Tamil script. The letters are geometrical and writing is linear, probably the best modern script in India. The Tamil alphabet has only 23 consonant letters. Unlike other Indian scripts, the Tamil Alphabet has no conjunct consonant clusters. For that they use a dot at top of the letter representing no vowel, equivalent to hasanta. From the South Indian branch the old Kanarese script developed around the eighth century; and from it modern Kanarese and Telegu characters, which are quite similar to each other. The Malayalam alphabet was derived from the Grantha. There were at least forty scripts derived from the Brahmi in India alone, of which only eight are used extensively today. In Sri Lanka the Singhalese characters are somewhat similar to South Indian signs but their language is derived from the Sanskrit.

V. INFLUENCE OF BRAHMI SYSTEM OVER ASIA

The Sino-Tibetan group of languages branched into the Chinese and the Tibeto-Burman group. The languages in the later group are Tibetan, Burmese, Manipuri, Bhotia, Lepcha, and many languages in the Himalayas, Eastern India, and Burma. The closely related Tai (Thai) group of languages includes Thai, Lao, and several other minor languages. Coulmas (112) says that "on linguistic grounds, one would expect that the Chinese writing system could be transferred with greatest ease to the languages most closely related to Chinese." There is no doubt that all these languages adapted the Brahmi system of writing because the Indian cultural influence dominated these countries. In retrospect, however, all of them were vastly benefitted by borrowing the Indian alphabetic writing system instead of thousands of Chinese characters.

Manipur is situated in the eastern area of India bordering Burma. The beautiful land is famous for its classical dance, as the originator of the game of polo, and above all for Arjuna, the hero of the great epic poem the *Mahabharata*, who fell in love with the princess Chitrangada of Manipur. Rabindranath Tagore probably reached the peak of his genius in the dance-drama *Chitrangada* (equivalent to opera mixed with dance) as a poet, composer, dramatist, and choreographer. Manipuris were converted to the Vaishnavism of Sri Chaitanya (1486-1534) of Bengal, carrying the Bengali alphabet in the eighteenth century, replacing the old Manipuri script.

TIBETAN ALPHABET

Buddhism spread from India to Tibet in the seventh century, along with many aspects of Indian civilization, including the Indian writing system. Based on the Gupta script, the Tibetan alphabet was created in 639 by the minister Thon-mi-Sam-bhota. The modification includes, /a/ has a full vowel sign (ཨ), while others, i (ི), u (ུ), e (ེ), o (ོ), have diacritical marks attached to the vowel sign for /a/, an excellent idea, which all other Brahmi derived alphabets should follow. Conjunct consonants are written the first above the second, in their full form, with little modification, without losing the shape of the characters. An unusual and useful feature is the use of a mark (') at the end of a word, thus separating words. For the four palatal signs for the borrowed sounds, ṭ, ṭh, ḍ , ṇ, they just turned 180 degrees the equivalent dental signs. The Tibetan alphabet, or its use, has changed little for over a 1,000 years, but the language has changed significantly over the period, causing differences between the sounds and the letters. The Tibetan language has tones but no tonal signs. However, without any tonal signs Tibetan can be read in context without much problem. Tibetan script, written mostly on Buddhism, probably is the most beautiful of all Brahmi group of alphabets, and the improvements show how much care have been taken on the script.

Fig. 12. TIBETAN ALPHABET

	Non-aspirated	aspirated	Non-aspirated	Nasal
velars	k ཀ	kh ཁ	g ག	ng ང
Palatals	c ཅ	ch ཆ	j ཇ	n̄ ཉ
Dentals	t ཏ	th ཐ	d ད	n ན
labials	p པ	p ཕ	b བ	m མ
Sibilants	ts ཙ	tsh ཚ	ds ཛ	
	w ཝ	ż ཞ	z ཟ	
Semivowels	y ཡ	r ར	l ལ	
	sh ཤ	s ས	h ཧ	

BRAHMI SYSTEM IN CENTRAL AND NORTH ASIA

From the Central Asian Gupta, Tokharian script developed, with two types, the Agnean and the Kuchean, in the area between the mountains of T'ien-shan and the river Tarim, now in China. From the Central Asian cursive Gupta script Khotanese evolved. Many manuscripts of Khotanese were found in the Caves of the Thousand Buddhas in Tun-huang, as well as in Kansu, Northwest China (Diringer, v. I, 275).

The Sogdians, centered on the prosperous trading cities of Samarkand and Bukhara, now in Uzbekistan, spoke a branch of the Persian language and used Sogdian script. This was used in the second half of the first millennium as the *lingua franca* of Central Asia. This area, and the Chinese province of Sinkiang was a melting pot of Indians, Tibetans, Turkik, Chinese, and Iranians (Diringer, 244). The letters of the Sogdian script are arranged as follows (Jensen, Fig. 408): a,(a), i, (i), o, (o,u,u), y,(z, q), g, k, i, j, r, l, t, d, c, s, s, z, n, p, (b), n, v, w, m, l., in the Indian phonetic order of letters with vowels and consonant signs separated. This order of letters also appears in all the Central and North Asian alphabets, for example, Uighurian, Galik, Mongolian, Kalmuk, Manchurian, Siberian and Buryat. (see Jensen, Figs. 408, 411, 412, and 419).

Jensen also tabulated the comparative signs, and phonetic values of the Aramaic, and the characters of the Sogdian, Uighurian, Galik, Mongolian, Kalmuck, and Manchurian. (Fig. 408-412). Jensen, however, admits that the Central and North Asian alphabets have "the order of the letters, which corresponds to that of the Indian alphabets, not the Semitic" (Ibid, 417). Although both Jensen and Diringer believe that these Asian alphabets came from the Aramaic or Syriac script, they find difficulty in matching the signs with the Aramaic letters. Jensen (410) theorizes that the "Sogdian script, in common with Syriac, is to be treated back to an older type of Aramaic script, which cannot be more precisely determined yet." The Buryat people, living around the Lake Baikal in Siberia, took the phonetic base of their alphabet from India, and the script from the Galik. The Buryats have maintained their love for learning from the Buddhist lamas; they have achieved a high level of education and are employed in the aircraft manufacturing industry. The Siberian alphabet was used along the rivers Obi and Yenisey, as well as in East Turkestan (Jensen, 422), and the phonetic order of the letters is of Indian origin, but the signs are suggestive of Old Sogdian script.

Under the Mongol Emperor Genghis Khan, the Uighurian language and its script became the official language of the state chancellery, and the records of Mongolian rulers were written in it into the fifteenth century (Jensen, 410). Under the direction of the Mongol Emperor, a lama designed a new alphabet, the Galik, on the basis of Sa-skya Pandit's alphabet, with five signs taken from the Tibetan. From the Galik the modern Mongolian script developed. A famous grand lama named Phans-pa was invited to China by the Mongol emperor Kublai Khan. The lama spread Buddhism to the royal court and used Tibetan square script for the Mongolian language (Diringer, 279). From the Mongolian script, the lama Zaya Pandit in 1648 developed the Kalmuck script for those people who settled on the lower Volga River (Ibid, 418) in Russia. Manchurians belong to the Tungus group of people, and their language is related to the Korean. The Manchu emperor in 1599 asked scholars to create a national alphabet, and they remodelled the Mongolian alphabet for the Manchu language. According to Jensen, the Manchurian language and script "were prescribed till the middle of the eighteenth century as official subjects of the state examinations in China" (Ibid, 419).

All these writings of the Central and Northern Asia have these characteristics: first, the phonetic order of the letters are of Indian origin, second, the shape of most of the characters were independently designed with some Tibetan influence, and third, they were written from top to bottom, and right to left, under the Chinese influence.

SPREAD OF BRAHMI SYSTEM TO SOUTHEAST ASIA

From the South Indian branch of the Brahmi about 25 scripts arose in all of Southeast Asia. Burmese script developed from the Pali alphabet of India. It has 13 signs for vowels and 32 signs for consonants. Almost all the letters look like a part of a circle. The Burmese language has three tones, for which there are signs. The Burmese orthography represents the sounds of old Burmese rather than the language that is spoken today.

The Tai (Thai) group of languages is closely related to the Sino-Tibetan group. The Thai language is written in a script derived from the Pali alphabet. The script has as many as 44 consonant signs, and are pronounced with a short /o/ instead of /a/. The signs for the vowels and diphthongs are used on the consonant signs as diacritical marks. The individual vowels are formed by attaching different diacritical marks on the letter *o*. Thai is a tonal language with five tones. There are four signs for tones, and the absence of a sign indicate the fifth tone.

The Cambodian language is in the Mon-Khmer group of Austro-Asiatic languages. The Hindu kingdom of Kambuja flourished between the ninth and twelfth century A.D., and the Cambodians built one of the architectural-sculptural masterpieces of the world, in the Hindu (Shiva) Temple of Ankor Wat. Their writing developed from the Grantha alphabet of south India, and the first appearance of the script is dated A.D. 604 (Diringer, v.1, 317). They have 32 signs for consonants, and 15 for vowels. The Mon-Khmer group of languages usually do not have tones. The Vietnamese language is also in the Mon-Khmer group but, influenced by the Chinese and Tai group of languages, gradually acquired six tones over 2,000 years. (Din-Hoa Nguyen, 777). The northern and central part of their country (Annam) was under China for over a 1,000 years, during that time they borrowed over half of their words from the Chinese. In the 14th century they started using Chinese characters. The old Hindu kingdom of Champa in South Vietnam used the Brahmi derived Champan alphabet in the later part of the first millennium, and when the kingdom decayed the alphabet also disappeared. Catholic missionaries introduced the Roman alphabet in the 17th century.

The Malaya-Polynesian group of languages extends from Malaya through Indonesia to the Philippines. In the past, dozens of Indian-based alphabets were used throughout the area. The Javanese Kavi script is still used in Java, the main and most populous island of Indonesia. The Javanese built the greatest Buddhistic architectural-sculptural masterpiece, in Borobudor in Central Java. Hinduism still flourishes in the beautiful island of Bali, and colorful Hindu festivals draw international audiences. The priests still use Sanskrit language in the temples. The islanders use the Balinese alphabet derived from the Grantha script. In the large islands of Sumatra, Batak script, and in Celebes, the Burginese characters are used. At present Bahasa (in Sanskrit *Bhasa* means language) Indonesia is the official state language of Malaya and Indonesia, and it is written in the Roman alphabet. Although it is the mother tongue of only 10% of the population, it is understood by 75% of the people. Tagalog and a few other languages in the Philippine Islands used to be written in the Indian derived alphabets. The Roman alphabet is gradually replacing the Indian derived scripts of Indonesia. Professor Diringer, in his book, *The Alphabet*, provides detailed account of the 35 Brahmi derived alphabets in the Southeast Asian countries, and presents the most magnificient collection of specimens of the scripts in the world. One should also consult Professor Jensen's detailed account of a large number of scripts, with numerous specimens; his comparison of different scripts is particularly helpful.

JAPANESE WRITING SYSTEMS

According to the Japanese tradition, a Korean scholar named Wani brought to Japan a large number of books on Buddhism, written in Chinese, around the fifth century. Starting from then almost all aspects of Chinese culture were adapted by the Japanese, along with the Chinese writing system. The Japanese language is totally different from the Chinese. The Japanese borrowed a very large numbers of Chinese words in Chinese characters from different parts of China at different times, pronouncing them mostly in the Japanese way. They also borrowed thousands of Chinese characters whose meaning was similar in Japanese; others had similar phonetic value. The Japanese devised "a writing system which is so complex", Sansom writes, "that it needs the aid of another system to explain it. There is no doubt that....as a practical instrument it is surely without inferiors." (Sansom, quoted by DeFrancis,140).

The other system is the syllabic Kana writing of native Japanese creation. Kana has two forms, Katakana and Hiragana. The syllabic writing is attributed to the Buddhist priest Ko'bo'daishi (774-835) (Jensen, 203).

The priest undoubtedly studied the Indian phonetics along with the Buddhist scriptures in Sanskrit and Pali. In one of the most interesting adaptations, the Japanese scholars found that in their language there are only just over one hundred syllables. With so few syllables, the Japanese writing system would be best served by syllabic characters rather than the alphabetic system of the Brahmi. Children are spared to construct thousands of syllables with consonants and vowels. Syllables are easier to learn, read, and write economically. They took the Indian system of phonetics, and arranged their syllabic characters with the vowels first and then the consonant-vowels (CV). Origin of a syllabic system from an alphabetic one goes against Gelb's theory; which says that in the development of writing, "it must pass through the stages of logography, syllabography, and alphabetography in this, and no other, order. Therefore, no writing can start with a syllabic or alphabetic stage unless it is borrowed, directly or indirectly, from a system which has gone through all the previous stages." (201). This may be essentially true, although, many scholars do not agree with Gelb, in the Egyptian-Phoenician-Greek group of writing which originated from the pictograms. However, it does not at all apply to the Brahmi alphabetic writing system which originated, as we have already shown from the analysis of the phonetic system of the Sanskrit language, and later supplied with individual geometric signs.

Kanazawa in 1907 first noticed the influence of the Sanskrit writing system on the Japanese Kana as well as on the Korean Han'gul. Since then many scholars have confirmed it. The order of the consonants bears witness to the influence of an Indic-inspired phonological analysis (Miller, quoted by Coulmas, 130). Both katakana and hiragana are based on the Indian phonetical structure modified for the Japanese language. The signs of the katakana are derived from manyogana, a Japanese sound based adaptation of the Chinese characters. Hiragana characters also derived from the same source but a cursive form of it. (Coulmas, 131).

Fig. 13. JAPANESE KATAKANA SYLLABLES

Vowels		ア A	イ I	ウ U	エ E	オ O
Consonants (Syllables)	Velar	カ ka	キ ki	ク ku	ケ ke	コ ko
	Palatal	サ sa	si	ス su	セ se	ソ so
	Dental	タ ta	チ tsi	ツ tsu	テ te	ト to
	(Nasal)	ナ na	ニ ni	ヌ nu	ne	ノ no
	Aspirant	ハ ha	ヒ hi	フ hu	ヘ he	ホ ho
Bilabial (Nasal)		マ ma	ミ mi	ム mu	メ me	モ mo
Semi-vowels		ヤ ya		ユ yu	エ ye	ヨ yo
		ラ ra	リ ri		レ re	ro
		wa	wi		ヱ we	ヲ wo

The voiced sounds were obtained by the nigori marks (") on the right upper corner of the unvoiced characters. For example, the voiced sound of ka (カ) is 'ga,' written as (ガ). Similarly, sa (サ) voiced za (ザ), ta (タ) voiced da (ダ). However, the sign for ha (ハ) is used for the unvoiced sound, pa (パ) with maru mark (°), and pa's voiced sound 'ba' (バ) with nigori mark is rather irregular. All other voiced sounds (za, da, ba, gi) also have similar nigori marks. With these basic 47 syllabic characters, 20 signs for the voiced sounds with nigori marks, five p's with five different vowels with maru marks, and one solitary consonant n, a total of 73 characters, the Japanese language can be written adequately.

Most of the borrowed Chinese words, pronounced in the Japanese way, are written in Chinese characters, although they can be written in katakana or the hiragana if one ignores large number of homonyms. Words borrowed from the English, and other languages changed so much in Japanese pronunciation that most of them also can be written in syllabic characters. For example, *nairon* for nylon, *torakku* for truck, *hoteru* for hotel, *rondon* for London, *girishia* for Greece, *kompyu'ta'* for computer, and thousands of other words. Even foreign names, the most difficult to write in a different script, is changed in the Japanese way, as with *firippu* for Philip, *po'ru* for Paul. Changing Japanese syllabic characters to purely alphabetic script would be a backward step, since learning to read and write in syllables is easier than with an alphabet as children are spared from the construction of syllables with consonant and vowel letters. The major problem in the Japanese language is the large number of homonyms, because of limited number of syllables; this cannot be improved by alphabetic writing. It is an ironic fact that while the Japanese developed the kana syllabic system, which almost perfectly suits their language, they ended up with one of the worst system of writing ever created, demonstrating the Japanese inability, or refusal, to make a clean break with the Chinese characters (DeFrancis,138). Here lies the fundamental solution: eliminate all the clumsy and complex Chinese characters from the Japanese orthography. My own suggestion is:

1) Use all the hiragana signs (47 characters and 29 with diacritical marks) for the 76 syllables, and the consonant 'n' as is done today;

2) Use the katakana signs without the vowel sounds of /a/, as consonants only, for example, ka, sa, ta,....for k, s, t..., particularly for foreign names or words. This will give the following consonants: k, s, sh, t, ch, h, m,y, r, w, g, z, j, d, b, p, and v. The total number of consonant signs, including 'n,' will be 18.

3) Split the Chinese characters, and take only the essential classifier, key or the radical signs needed to help to disambiguate the meaning of the homonymous words. Most of the 214 Chinese classifiers are not needed, and so can be discarded. Some new classifiers, and few other extra syllabic and alphabetic signs, may be created. The advantage of this system is that all these signs are already known to all literate Japanese. For elementary school teachers it would be very easy to learn and teach. Best of all, the Japanese children would not need to memorize even a single complicated Chinese character. This will make Japanese syllabic Kana system one of the best orthograph in the world.

KOREAN WRITING SYSTEMS

The Korean, an agglutinative language, is totally different from the Chinese. Most probably, Korean is related to the Manchu, Mongol, and Turkik languages, and possibly the Uralo-Altaic languages, such as the Finnish and Hungarian, and the Dravidian languages of South India (Kim Chin-U, 16). Chinese writing system is particularly unsuitable for the Korean language. The Koreans tried to improve their orthography by adapting a system of 36 signs based on the Sanskrit writing system in Chinese characters, called *cha-mo*, in 543 A.D. (Jensen, 211).

Around 1446 King Sejong gathered a group of scholars to create a new and simple writing system for all levels of Koreans. The King, along with these scholars, searched for models in different systems available to them. The most easily available was, of course, the Buddhist scriptures written in Pali or Sanskrit. Many of the Korean Buddhist scholars certainly studied the Indian system of phonetics. Marshal Pihl (p.119) says that the great achievement of Korean phonetic script Han'gul, and highly developed linguistic science of Western Europe owes much to the same Indian source. The Koreans also studied the Mongolian and the Tibetan alphabets, both of which originated from the Indian system. Han'gul seems to be the only script in which the shapes of the symbols suggest location of the articulation of the sound (Taylor, 68). For example, the /g/ sign (ㄱ) shows the tongue touching the soft palate, and the sign for /n/ (ㄴ) the tongue touching the teeth; the same technique is used in /d/, /t/,/dd/, and /r,l/ (Ibid, 69). Intelligent use of anatomical design for scripts is unique in the history of writing. Furthermore, characters are simple geometric forms, straight and vertical lines, and circles. Inspite of having such an excellent alphabetic system, it was looked down, and the Chinese characters dominated because of conservatism. The North Korean president, about four decades ago, abolished the use of Chinese characters for the Korean language. South Korea still uses a mixture of Chinese and Han'gul. Probably within one or two generations, South Koreans will also abandon thousands of Chinese characters.

The phonetic order of the Korean Han'gul is modified from the Brahmi system. The old Korean order of consonant letters was closer to that of the Indian system : k, kh, ng, t, th, n, p, ph, m, ch, chh, s(d), h, r (l), rh in the great Korean Encyclopedia Mun-hen-pi-go published in 1770 A.D. (Jensen, 214). This order is also in the Chemo syllabic system in China, which "goes back to the Indian model" (Ibid).

Fig. 14.

THE KOREAN ALPHABET

Vowels:								
ㅏ	ㅓ	ㅗ	ㅜ	ㅡ	ㅣ	ㅐ	ㅔ	ㅓ
a	u	o	iu	oo	ee	ae	e	ui

Consonants	Tense Unvoised	Lax voiced	Tense Aspirated	Nasal
Glottal	k ㄱ	gg ㄲ	k' ㅋ	n ㄴ
Dental	t ㄷ r/l ㄹ	dd ㄸ	t' ㅌ	m ㅁ
Labial	p ㅂ	bb ㅃ	p' ㅍ	
Sibilant	s ㅅ	ss ㅆ		ㅇ (initial - no sound)
Palatal	ch ㅈ	j j ㅉ	ch' ㅊ	(final - ng)
	h ㅎ			

The Han'gul has been described as "perhaps the most scientific system of writing in general use in any country" (Reischaur,1960), and "the world's best alphabet" (Vos,1964, p.31). Hubert (quoted by Diringer, 444) considers it "the most perfect phonetic system....only one of its vowels is used for more than one sound....of its consonants, only one is used to represent two sounds, and these sounds of l and r." Diringer (Ibid) disagreeing says, "The opinion that the Korean alphabet is phonetically perfect is exaggerated, for it has more sounds than written characters. There are no separate signs for the sounds g, b, d, j, although these sounds exist in Korean, and represented by the letters k, p, t, and ch." Furthermore, as regards the double signs, Sampson (123) says, "Some combination of these letters are better treated as separate graphic units." "The contrast between short and long vowels...has never been indicated in Han'gul writing....although length is still constrastive today in most Korean dialects, including the standard dialect of Seoul" (Ibid, 132). Although Han'gul is not a perfect alphabetic system it has been able to express the Korean language well, and after the South Koreans discard the Chinese characters Korean writing would be one of the best writing system.

Every country surrounding China, even parts of China itself, adapted the Indian phonetic writing system. These countries and areas are Tibet, Uighur (Sinkiang), Mongolia, Manchuria, Korea (Han'gul), Japan (Kana); Burma, Thailand, Cambodia, Laos, Southern Vietnam, the islands of Indonesia, Phillipines; Sri Lanka, Nepal, Bhutan; Afghanistan, Persia, Uzbekistan, the Volga basin in Russia, the Obi and Yenisa basin, and around the Baikal sea in Siberia. These languages are in many linguistic groups: Tibeto-Burman, Tai, Mon-Khmer, Polynesian, Japanese, Korean, Mongolian, Tungusic, and Indo-European (Persian and Uzbek). Of course, all the writings of India developed from the Brahmi alphabet. China developed in 543 A.D. the *Chamo*, a syllabic system with 36 signs, built on the model of the Sanskrit stock of sounds; and in the 14th century this system was shortened to 31 signs and was called *Hong-mu* (Jensen, 211). Things changed after the Islamic invasions, the Sogdians, Uighurs, and all Central Asians, Persians, Pakistanis, Urdu speakers in India adapting the Arabic script. The areas in the old Russian republics, Uzbekistan, Kazakstan and other republics replaced the Indian system with the Cyrillic script for political reasons.

VI. SYLLABIC-'MEANING' SYSTEMS: SUMERIAN, CHINESE & MAYAN

The Sumerians, over 5,000 years ago, were the first people to create a civilization. It was on the hostile valley of the Tigris and Euphrates Rivers, now the lower half of Iraq. During the summer, the sun mercilessly scorched the barren land, baking the soil hard so that no vegetation could survive. In the spring, rain and melting snow from the mountains often caused unpredictable and extensive floods overflowing the rivers. This was hardly a suitable land for our first. civilization. However, this land had a few redeeming features: for example, millions of years of overflowing rivers had brought valuable deposit of silts, making the land fertile. There were plenty of fishes in the rivers and marshy areas, as well as their predetor, waterfowls, to add an extra amount of protein to their agricultural products. The rivers were helpful in transport and trade.

It is the organizing genius of the Sumerians, a people not related linguistically or racially to any other tribe, to dig canals and build dams to irrigate their dry land to produce a significant surplus of agricultural products on which they could support a large number of skilled people to build a major civilization. The Sumerians were the first to create the two greatest pillars of civilization, a writing system and mathematics. They were also the first to develop many abstract ideas as well as scores of practical tools. Babylonians inherited all aspects of the Sumerian civilization. King Hammurabi ascended the throne in 1750 B.C., and gave the first codified law, Gilgamesh is the first epic poem, the story of world wide flood, monumental architecture and sculpture, government by elected rulers, schools and libraries, the wheeled vehicle, and scores of other elements of civilization are the gifts of the Sumerians (Kramer,161,ff). "Down through the millennia, Mesopotemia still speaks to the world....from the blossoming of ideas, institutions and techniques that resulted have come major tools of civilization, since altered in detail but never in basic concept." says Kramer (163).

Denise Schmandt-Besserat has done extensive research on the origin of the Sumerian writing and numbers developed since the eighth millennium B.C. Her ideas are based on an enormous collection of clay tokens inside clay envelopes, beautifully reproduced in two large volumes (1992). The simple geometrical forms of the plain tokens usually showed the numbers; the complex token had incised on its surface pictograms indicating the nature of the items counted. "The duality of our own writing system which uses numerals (ideograph) and letters (phonetic signs) was presaged in the first reckoning devise using tokens. Plain tokens and impressed signs brought about the use of abstract numerals, whereas the complex tokens and,....incised pictographs slowly evolved to the acquisition of phonetic values" (39-40).

There is enough epigraphic evidence to follow the gradual evolution of the Sumerian script. The Sumerians started with the pictures of man, woman, animals and common objects to communicate magical or religious functions. These pictures gradually became highly stylized. As they used easily available wet clay to write, or rather press on with a reed stylet, cut in such a way that it had a triangular tip, the marks on the clay were wedge shaped. These clay tablets were dried in the sun, and have survived today. These stylized pictures were words (logograms) of man, woman, animals, hills, *et cetera*; they were not adequate to write the Sumerian language. Sometime around 3,000 B.C., in Jemdet Nasr or in Uruk, a genius got the idea of using the name of the object, or part of it, for not only the meaning of the object but also for all ideas or objects with the same sound. For example, a picture of an arrow ( ), pronounced 'ti' in Sumerian, means arrow as well as life as a homophonous word. Since it is impossible to draw a picture of 'life,' the Sumerians used the picture of an arrow to indicate life. This rebus principle was used by the Egyptians also probably a hundred years later. This was the essential step for the partial writing to grow into a full writing system.

At the beginning, the word signs were used just to remind other scribes a general idea, the number of cattle, or the amount of wheat, without following the grammar or the order of the words in their language. Nevertheless, during this period the Sumerians had the capability of using their script to represent most of the sounds of their language. Only over the centuries did their graph represent Sumerian language adequately in proper word order and grammar. Sumerian was an agglutinative language, and to its word roots, monosyllabic without internal changes, particles were attached which also kept their forms without changes. Most of the syllables were consonant-vowel-consonant (CVC) though CV or VC was also common. Probably only a few hundred were commonly used. A Sumerian proverb runs, "A scribe whose hand matches the mouth, he is indeed a scribe" (Green, quoted by DeFrancis 81). Some syllables were not represented at all; in other extreme 22 different syllabic characters were used for one syllabic sound, 'du.' Two syllables, CV and VC, could be joined to make CVC, for example, da + am = dam (DeFrancis, 81); it would have been possible to express all the Sumerian language in a relatively simple manner with only 132 syllabograms (Ibid, 82). Sumerians over the time reduced the number of signs from about 2,000 to about 400. When the meaning in a homonymous word was not clear they used the signs for meaning (determinatives). There were about a dozen or so determinatives that showed the category of meaning, man, plant, stars, and others. They also used 'phonetic complements' by attaching a phonetic symbol to the word like the Egyptians. However, over the years Sumerian writing improved by increasing the number and use of syllabic signs, and by reducing those for meaning. The syllabic signs comprised between 36 and 54 percent in Sumerian texts (Civil, quoted by DeFrancis,84).

Akkadians conquered Sumer and settled there around the later part of the third millennium B.C. They adapted many aspects of the Sumerian civilization, including their writing system. Akkadians spoke a Semitic language totally different from the Sumerians. The syllabic writing was a misfit for the Akkadians. They took the signs for the syllables and determinatives from the Sumerians, and used for their language making it a highly complicated and inefficient writing system. Nonetheless, because of the Akkadians' political power it was extensively used in the Middle East.

CHINESE WRITING SYSTEM

China developed on the valley of the Yellow River over 3,500 years ago the fourth civilization, after the Sumer, Egypt, and India, on the Tigris-Euphrates, the Nile, and the Indus Valley, respectively. The Chinese language is the most important branch of the Sino-Tibetan-Burman group of languages; all of them have tones (variation of pitch) and a highly restricted syllabic structure. The tones are an integral part of the syllables and important factor to differentiate their meaning. Mandarin speech has four tones, and the syllabic structure consists of a nuclear vowel with an optional initial consonant and a final 'ng' or 'n' consonant only (Li and Thompson,814). There are five different major language-dialect groups of Chinese: Mandarin dominates with 70% of the speakers, and the others are Wu, Yei, Hakka, and Min. They are mutually unintelligible (Ibid, 813). DeFrancis says, "It is a widespread myth that Chinese characters cut across the boundaries of speech....It takes more effort for a Cantonese to learn to read and write the standard Beijing language than for a Spaniard to learn French (95). Chinese is an isolating language, which means that it lacks grammatical inflections, most words have one fixed form, which does not change according to number, gender, tense, case, mood and other categories (Li & Thompson, 824).

The earliest pictographic characters were written on bones or tortoise shells during the Shan Dynasty (1500-1045 B.C.). From 1200 B.C. the characters were written on silk, bamboo, wood and brass. (DeFrancis, 99). However, the basic principle of the characters has not changed during the last two thousand years.

Sampson (145) says that "A graph of the Chinese writing system stands not for a unit of pronunciation but for a morpheme, a minimal meaningful unit of the Chinese language. Since Chinese, like English or any other language, has thousands of morphenes in its vocabulary, the Chinese script includes thousands of graphs. "If two morphemes are pronounced identically, which happens frequently," he continues,"they will normally have two separate graphs which may not share even a partial resemblance."(145). Also, because each morpheme is one syllable long, Sampson identifies Chinese writing system as logographic (word signs). Furthermore, Chinese characters stand for words and not directly for things or ideas; it symbolizes units of a particular spoken language, the Chinese (Ibid, 149). Occasionally, for abstract ideas rebus principle is used as in the Sumerians and the Egyptian writing. For example, a sign for wheat, called 'leg' (來) is also used for the homonym meaning 'to come.' (Coulmas,

99). The Chinese scribes also developed signs like the Sumerian determinatives for areas of meaning. There are traditionally 214 classifier (significs), for man, mouth, tree, etc. Each Chinese character has two elements, the syllabic sign, and the sign for the meaning (semantic).

In Chinese language the syllabic sounds at present are some 1,277 counting tones and about 400 not counting tones (DeFrancis,116). Mandarin Chinese could have been written phonetically with this number of characters. And if required, the 214 classifiers could have been used to cover the areas of meaning in homonymous words, with a total of about 1,500 characters. The important difference between the Chinese and the Sumerian or the Egyptian is that the Chinese incorporated the phonetic elements into the semantic signs which could not be dissociated. This caused multiplication of numbers of two different elements of signs, namely, the phonetic and the 'meaning' rather than addition, as in the Sumerian or the Egyptian. For example, if we take about 400 syllabic signs without tone, and about 200 classifiers glued together, we get about 80,000 (400 x 200) characters. Even if one uses only half or a quarter of these characters, they comprise colossal numbers. If, however, they had kept the sound and the meaning signs separated, even with 1,300 syllables with tones and 214 classifier, the total number would have been more reasonable: 1,514 (1,300 + 214) characters, instead of tens of thousands. Furthermore, DeFrancis writes, "Throughout its history the actual sound-to-symbol relationship in Chinese has approximated on the syllabic level the much maligned situation in English on the phonemic level. In contrast to the one-to-one relationship, where there is close correspondence between sound and symbol, both writing systems are characterized by a highly complex many-to-many relationship" (119). According to Y.R. Chao, the Chinese writing is 25% phonetic whereas in English it is 75%. (Ibid, 111).

DeFrancis cites (111) research which indicates that by memorizing the pronunciation of the 895 phonetic elements selected by Southhill, one can guess in 66 percent of the cases the pronunciation of any given characters in a modern text. DeFrancis (113) further stipulates that completely useful phonetic characters number 25%; generally useful, 17%; contextually useful ones, 24%; and useless phonetic ones, 33%. DeFrancis concludes that, "Chinese spelling as represented by its phonetic elements is erratic, inefficient, and difficult to master" (114). Furthermore, the Sumerians gradually reduced the number of signs to about 400. In contrast, the number of characters during the Shang Dynasty was only 977, which increased to 9,353 in the second century, and grew to 48,641 in the great imperial Kangsu dictionary in the 18th century (Ibid, 99). The classifier sometimes helps the meaning, but at other times it provides only a dim clue, and often gives no indication of the meaning whatsoever (Coulmas,103). Thus the classifiers (signs for meaning) played "only a limited role in semantic decoding" (Ibid,104). Sampson (156-7) points out succinctly that a Chinese has to memorize each character separately; both for the sound and the meaning, "will give him many hints and clues to help him remember, but the information they supply is far too patchy and unreliable to enable him to *predict* what the graph for a given spoken word will be, or even which spoken word will correspond to a graph that he encounters for the first time". Chinese characters, written with one to 25 strokes, is the most difficult script ever devised. No writing system in history ever needed tens of thousands complicated signs to memorize. Sumerians and Egyptians kept the numbers to a few hundred. "One of the most important elements making visual distinctiveness in Roman script" observes Sampson, "is the presence of 'ascenders' in letters such as <b f k t> (as well as dots of <i j>) and 'descenders' in <g y p>, which stand out from the body of a word and make for greater recognizability" (94). In contrast, most Chinese characters are squares with monotonous regularity, and the outer shape rarely gives any clue to its sound or meaning. To learn a few hundred characters of the Egyptians or the Sumerians, not to mention the letters of any alphabet is immeasurably easier than learning the multi-stroked thousands of Chinese characters. We have already discussed that almost all the languages in the Chinese-Tibetan linguistic group have adapted the Indian alphabetic system far more successfully, with or without the signs for the tones. The Vietnamese have taken the Roman alphabet. North Koreans have already abandoned the Chinese characters, and it is only a matter of time before the South Koreans also will reject them. The Japanese are deliberately reducing the numbers of Chinese characters in their kana-kanji mixed orthography. Even in China a Romanised Pinyin system has developed to suplement the Chinese characters as well as the number of Chinese characters are reduced.

MAYAN WRITING SYSTEM

Mayans were the only people in the Americas to create an original and full civilization, including a system of writing. This shows that civilization and writing can develop without any influence from other civilized nations. Mayan civilization extended from the Yucatan Peninsula of Mexico to Guatemala and Honduras. During the pre-classical period, extending from about 1,000 B.C. to 250 A.D., Mayans built pyramids including one of the largest structure of the world at El Mirador in Guatemala (Houston, 21). In the classical era, extending from c.250 to 900 A.D., Mayan writing developed from the pictograph-through logogram, syllabic characters, rebus principle, phonetic complements, and determinative-to a full writing system by 400 A.D. Without any outside influence they followed the path of the Sumerians, the Egyptians and the Chinese. In Mayan language most of the roots are monosyllabic which combined with monosyllabic prefixes and postfixes form nouns and verbs (DeFrancis,123). The Mayan language has 36 consonants and six vowels, for which their orthography had 5,300 different signs. The same sound could be represented by different signs, and some symbols had more than one sound. Their phonetic elements were glued to the 'meaning' elements as is the Chinese, rather than the separated units in the Sumerian and the Egyptian writing. As with the Egyptian hieroglyphs aesthetic consideration dictated the position and the size of the characters. The Mayans, by 400 A.D., could write their language with only the syllabic signs; but like the Sumerians and Egyptians, they continued to use the pictogram, logogram, and the determinatives.

VII. LITERACY AND CIVILIZATIONS

Spoken languages are among the greatest elements in the development of the human mind, which separates man from all other living being. The gradual development of anatomical structures in the auditory, laryngeal, buccal, nasal, and respiratory organs, as well as masterly neurophysiological coordination by the different parts of the brain are the result of genetic transmission. Learning the mother tongue is automatic and univers al except with rare physical, mental or social deficit. In contrast, writing systems are human creation, the ultimate goal is to record the speech as simply and clearly as possible. Most scholars would agree that alphabetic writing covering all the phonemes (sounds) of the language with only one individual sign for each sound is the ideal.

Most orthographies represent more or less the modern sounds of the languages. They may be called phonetic or phonemic. English and French are the best example of orthographies which represent the medieval sounds of the languages. They may be termed as lexical or etymological. Is it not tragic that most people in the world try to learn these two greatest modern languages should have the unnecessary hurdle of memorizing and mispronouncing the two most difficult alphabetic orthographies? However, some scholars maintain that the English orthgraphy is "a near optimal system for the lexical presentation of English words." (Chomsky and Halle p.49). Vachek and the Prague school of linguists think that the irregulaties of spelling English words, not only give the sound but also their meaning. For example, the same sound with different spellings give different meaning: 'rite' (ritual), 'right' (correct or direction) 'write' (inscribe), 'wright' (playwright). The Sumerian, Egyptian, Chinese, and the Mayan writings also have 'meaning' along with the sound of the word. Haas of Manchester, England has similar view on the English writing system

There are scholars who exaggerate the effect of the alphabet on different aspects of civilizations. The extreme examples are seen in McLuhan, Logan, and other works. Logan (49) believes that the main features of Western civilization - for example, logical thinking, deductive reasoning, progressiveness, geometry, natural law, codified law, and monotheism, developed due to alphabet. He also thinks that because of their system of writing the Chinese failed to develop any of the aspects of Western civilization. In contrast, the Chinese developed analogical and inductive reasoning, concrete, intuitive, mystical, space-oriented, traditional, concrete science, and the harmony of nature. Logan does not give any evidence why these differences are mainly, or even minimally, due to alphabet, and not due to hundreds of other known and unknown factors.

Many people, including scholars, believe that alphabet is the cause of widespread literacy; and pre-alphabetic writing having "such great complexity, only a scholar with years of arduous training and high intellect learned to read and write with facility,....the invention of the alphabet provided a new system of writing of breathtaking simplicity" (Cross, 77). He continues, "A person could now learn to read and write in a matter of days or weeks." Cross (78) also writes, "Literacy spread rapidly and broadly....and with it democratization of culture." Everyone wished that was true, for it would have eradicated illiteracy thousands of years ago in parts of the world where alphabetic writing was available. Unfortunately, this never happened. It takes for an avarage person to learn to read and write adequately his mother tongue in alphabetic writing many months, If not years.

Harris in his book, *Ancient Literacy*, probably the most extensive study on this subject, provides a much better assessment. "From 480 B.C. onwards at least 15% of adult male population reached the level of semiliteracy or some higher level, and a very substantial portion of this 15% was able to write easily. Therefore we can probably take it that 5% or more of the total adult population (including women and slaves) was literate" (328). This is, of course, centuries after the Greeks developed an excellent alphabetic system. Harris also estimates that the literates and semiliterates among the citizens of Athens exceeded 6,000, when the total population of Attica was over 100,000 (114)." Not only was the literacy rate among the citizens lower than that of most illiterate countries today, it was much worse among the non-citizens, the women and the slaves in Greece. "There is no evidence at all," Harris maintains, "that in the classical period girls attended schools in Athens. The few women who were literate were the daughters of well-to-do families, teaching done by a literate slave or heteiri" (Ibid, 96). If the literacy rate was so low in enlightened Athens, durig the best of times, with an alphabet, one can guess how widespread was illiteracy in the ancient and medieval times around the world. At least, in ancient times a small percent of literate leaders could create great and original civilizations with complicated writing systems, for example, the Sumerians, Egyptians, Indians (Harappans), Chinese and the Mayans. However, a system of writing is essential for the origin and growth of any civilization. The solitary exception is the Inca civilization.

In fact, there is little relationship between literacy and the alphabet. Some of the alphabetic writing areas of Africa have lowest literacy rates. The Japanese Kanji (borrowed Chinese characters) system of writing is considered by many experts as the most complex system ever devised; still the literacy rate of Japan is among the highest in the world. A perfect alphabetic system is needed to remove the tears and frustrations of children, to make learning fun, to reduce memorization by rote, and to save time to pursue more interesting subjects and games. Also, a good phonetic alphabet would significantly reduce the number of functional illiterates. In the Japanese syllabic kana system the literacy rate is certainly the highest in the world. However, in Japanese kanji (Chinese characters) there must be a significant number of semiliterates or functionally illiterates. The firugana (side kana), the smaller kana signs, used next to the Chinese characters, to show the sound of the complex Chinese signs help not only the Japanese children, but also semiliterate adults.

Widespread literacy is a modern phenomenon, and there are many factors, by far the most important one is the economic development of the country which can afford, and is willing to establish a free and compulsory educational system. Unfortunately, in most countries education has low priority compared to the military.

Who needs to learn to read and write, and perform useful arithmetical calculations in modern times? Everyone would agree that every soul on our planet need them so that not only can he or she function in a society but also maintain and help civilizations to grow. As one often has observed, a fluent reader in Spanish or German, with rational orthographies, in contrast to English or even Japanese, apparently reads as fluently with understanding irrespective of the quality of the orthographies. Of course, after mastering the script, frequent readers use the shapes of the words, phrases, lines for understanding. A very fast reader uses even paragraphs or a page as a unit for reading. When we start to learn to read the sounds and signs are equally important, but as we become fluent, visual variation of shapes of the words and phrases dominates. It is probably true that once one has mastered an orthography, there is no significant difference in the speed of reading, whether it is phonetic or even Japanese Kanji. However, in learning, and particularly in writing, there is always a fundamental difference between a high quality phonetic alphabet and a partially phonetic one. Admittedly, there are great difficulties in arranging such experiments with proper control. Frequent readers would master any orthography, whether it is perfectly phonetic, without vowels, has much less visual differentiation among the signs, or has highly complex Chinese characters.

It is a great surprise that a perfect writing system does not replace a poor one. Only religious or political influence can do that. Any system of writing is essential for the origin, development and maintenance of civilizations, with the solitary exception of the Inca civilization. Strangely, as we have seen, the quality of the writing system apparently does not make any difference in the origin or the growth of any civilization. In contrast, as we will see in the next section, superior quality mathematical concepts always replace the inferior ones, and the highest quality has the profound effect on the growth of civilizations.

REFERENCES

Allen, W. Sidney, *Phonetics in Ancient India,* 1965. Oxford U.P. London

" " " , *Vox Latina,* 1978 Cambridge U.P., London

" " " , *Vox Graeca*, 1991, Cambridge University Press, London

Bandhopaddhay, Asit K., *Bangla Mudran* (Bengali Printing) 1981, Calcutta

Bloomfield, Leonard, *Language*, 1933, New York

Branch, Michael, *Finnish,* in *The World's Major Languages* (WML), Editor, Comrie, Bernard, 1990, Oxford U.P., New York

Budge, Earnest A. Wallis, *An Egyptian Hieroglyphic Dictionary*, 2 volumes, Dover Publ. New York

" " ", *Egyptian Language*, 1963, London

Chadwick J., *Linear B and Related Scripts,*1987. Cambridge U.P., London

Chatterjee, Suniti K. *The Origin and Development of the Bengali Language,* 1970 (reprint) in 3 volumes. London

Coedes, G., *Les Etats Hindouises d'Indochine et d'Indonesie,* 1948. Paris

Coomaraswamy, A.K., *History of Indian and Indonesian Art,*1927

Coulmas, Florian, *Writing Systems of the World,* 1991, Cambridge, Mass

Cross, Frank M., *The Invention and Development of Alphabet,* In *The Origin of Writing,* 1989. Univ. Of Nebraska, Lincoln

Davis, W.V., *Egyptian Hieroglyphs*, 1989, California U.P., Berkeley

DeFrancis, John, *Visible Speech,* 1989, Univ. of Hawaii, Honolulu

Dinh-Hoa Nguen, *Vietnamese*, in *The World's Major Languages,* Ed. Comrie Bernard, 1990, Oxford U.P. New York

Diringer, David, *The Origin of Alephbeth*, 1960. London

" " *The Alphabet, A Key to the History of Mankind,*1968. London

Driver, G.R., *Semetic Writing,* From Pictograph to Alphabet, 1954. Oxford. U.P., London

Edgerton,, William F., *Egyptian Phonetic Writing, from its Invention to the close of the Nineteenth Dynasty*, 1940 J. American Oriental Society

Fischer, Henry G., *The origin of Egyptian Hieroglyphs*, 1989, in *The Origin of Writing*, ed. by Senner.

Gaur, Albertine, *A History of Writing.* 1984,. London

Gelb, I. J., *A study of writing*, 1963, Univ. of Chicago

Green, John N., *Spanish, in Worlds Major Languages*, Ed. Comrie,1987. N.Y.

Harris, William, *Ancient Literacy,* 1989, Cambridge, Mass.

Houston, S.D., *Maya Glyphs*, 1989. Univ. of California.

Haas, W. *Writing without letters* (Ed.). 1970, Univ. of Manchester, England.

Jeffrey, L.H., *Local Scripts of Archaic Greece*, 1960. Oxford U. P., London.

Jensen, Hans, *Sign, Symbol and Script,* 1970, London.

Kachru, Braj B., *The Other Tongue, English Across Cultures,* 1982. Univ. of Illinois, Chicago, Urbana.

Kanazawa, S., *Uber den Einfluss des Sanskrits auf das Japanische und Koreanische Schriftsystem,* 1907. Tokyo.

Katzner, Kenneth, The Languages of the World, 1975 New York

Kim Chin-U, The Korean Language,UNESCO, 1983 Seaol.

Kramer, Samuel K., *Cradle of Civilization,* 1969, New York.

Krom,I.J., *Inleiding tot de Hindoo-Javaansche Kunst*, 1923.

Logan, Robert K., *The Alphabet effect,* 1986. New York.

Meltzer, E.S., *Remarks on Ancient Egyptian Writing,* Processing of Visible Language, vol.1, 1980, New York.

Moss, Elbert R., *Phonetics: History and Interpretation,* 1964, New Jersey

Nakanishi, Akira, Writing Systems of the World,1992 Rutland, Vermont.

Pihl, Marshall, in *The Korean Language,* UNESCO, 1983 Seaol

Sampson, Geoffrey, *Writing Systems*, 1985. Stanford University.

Schmandt-Besserat, Denise, *Two Precursors of Writing. In Origins of Writing,* Ed. by Wayne M. Senner, 1991. Univ. of Nebraska, Lincoln.

Tagore, Rabindranath, *Bangla Bhasa Parichay* (Introduction to Bengali Language) 1936, Calcutta.

Vachek, J. *Written Language: General Problems and Problems of English*, 1973. The Hague.

SECTION TWO

ARITHMETIC

"Arithmetic is the foundation of all mathematics, pure or applied," explains Tobias Dantzig. "It is the most useful of all sciences, and there is no other branch of human knowledge which is more widely spread among the masses" (36).

In this book arithmetic means calculations with numerical quantities, denoted by abstract symbols with rules of operation. Both numbers (ordinal) and arithmetic are used in ways most people understand. Arithmetic is essential for the origin and the development of all civilizations, and without it our modern civilization is virtually unthinkable. The abstract study of numbers, such as the theory of numbers that developed from Pythagoras (sixth century B.C.) to Srinivasa Ramanujan (1887-1920), is outside the scope of this book.

The earliest civilizations of Sumer and Egypt provided evidence that all their numbers had, as ours do, three properties: abstract symbols, quantity, and computational ability. From finger counting to computer calculations, the increasing capability of computation has been crucial in the growth of civilizations, by enabling acurate record keeping in agricultural, manufacturing, trade, finance, and other economic activities. The importance of computation in our civilization cannot be overestimated.

All numbers have quantities, except zero. Zero is not a quantity, rather, zero quantity is circumlocution. A zero in the numerals or in words (Sunya or zero) has only limited usefulness, but the number '0' in abstract sign, within and outside the numerals with all the rules of operation, becomes an extraordinarily powerful and useful mathematical entity. Negative numbers are also different from all numbers, being less than zero; but with the known rules of computation they are also very useful in mathematics. Finally, the third component of a number is abstract symbols. Without them arithmetical calculation is inefficient and clumsy. Ancient Indians used the alphabet and words to express "numbers," but they rarely used them for calculations. Without calculation there can be no arithmetic.

According to Denise Schmandt-Besserat, in a manner similar to the origin of the characters in the Sumerian language, abstract number symbols in Sumer originated from clay tokens (p. 39). Each cylindrical clay token ( ) represented one unit, a sphere ( ) represented ten, and each disc ( ) represented one hundred. They were obviously in the decimal system. There is much evidence of pre-civilized peoples counting numbers on bones, wood, rocks, and other hard surfaces. (Flegg, 37 ff.). The Incas used an ingenious system of knots on strings (quipa) to keep all kinds of numerical records of their empire. Interestingly, the quipas were in the decimal system.

Fig.15. DEVELOPMENT OF ARITHMETICAL SYMBOLS & DECIMAL SYSTEM

	1	2	3	4	5	6	7	8	9	10
SUMER 3,100 B.C.	𒁹	𒈫	𒐈	𒐉	𒐊	𒐋	𒐌	𒐍	𒐎	𒌋
EGYPT 3,000 B.C.	I	II	III	IIII	III II	III III	IIII III	IIII IIII	IIIII IIII	∩
INDIA Harappa 2,500 B.C.	I	II	III	IIII	IIIII	III III	IIII III	IIII IIII	IIIII IIII	ꓤ
Asoka 250 B.C.	—	=	≡	¥	ɲ	ɛ	ℸ	Ч	2	∝
Kharoṣṭhi 250 B.C.	I	II	III	X	IX	IIX	IIIX	XX	IXX	?
Bhojdeva 870 A.D.	१	२	३	४	५	६	७	८	९	१०
CHINA 1,400 B.C.	一	二	三	亖	㐅	介	十	八	九	
Tung Hua 400 A.D.	I	II	III	IIII						
(Modern)	一	二	三	四	五	六	七	八	九	十
MAYA (300 A.D.)	•	••	•••	••••	—	• —	•• —	••• —	•••• —	=

Almost all ancient arithmetical symbols were in vertical or horizontal lines in units of ten (decimal). However, Sumerians added units of sixty, and the Mayans had units of twenty. Each cylindrical clay token or line curved on wood probably represented one finger. As people often counted with ten fingers most pre-civilized people used units of ten (decimal). The theory that the vertical and horizontal lines for numbers and the decimal systems originated in one civilization and later spread to other civilizations lacks evidence, and the theory of multifocal origins seems to be correct.

VIII. SUMERO-BABYLONIAN ARITHMETIC

The Sumerians were the first civilization before 3,000 B.C. to create written arithmetic, and with their cultural descendants, the Babylonians, they raised arithmetic to a level far superior to what any other people accomplished until the seventh century A.D. Since the Babylonians borrowed almost all aspects of the Sumerian civilization, it is difficult to decide which parts of the Sumerian arithmetic were taken by the Babylonians. They started by using only two signs for their arithmetical numbers, a vertical line representing the number one, and an angle for the number 10. They wrote by pressing a stylet on soft wet clay, which made the signs appear wedge-shaped, like Y, and < . They used the decimal system only for numbers below 60. For example,

1, 2, 3, 4, 5, 6, 7, 8, 9   < 10   << 20   <<< 30   <<<< 40   <<<<< 50

Above sixty, however, they used a position or place-value system with the base of sixty (sexagesimal system) instead of our ten. For example, their symbol for 3 was three symbols of one attached at the top, YYY; and if unattached at the top, Y Y Y, the same three symbols for one denoted third place (60 x 60) + in second place (60 x 1) + in first place 1 equal to 3600 + 60 +1 = 3,661, by using place-value in units of 60. Our equivalent in deciimals is 100 +10 +1= 111. When they had to write 3601 they used the same symbols but in a different way: Y   Y. The first symbol is in our hundredth position but their 60x60 = 3600 position; the gap without any quantity is in the second position, equivalent to our zero in the second position; and the last symbol for one at the end is exactly like our one at the end of our numerals. The invention of the place-value system was one of the greatest achievements in mathematics, and the Babylonians developed it long before 1800 B.C. The well-known historian of mathematics Neugebauer (5) compared the invention of the place-value system to the invention of the alphabet. Babylonians could thus express and compute very large numbers with only a few symbols for astronomical works.

Sometimes the scribes did not keep a measured distance for the gap in their numerals, and thus there was often confusion as to whether there were one or two gaps or none at all. About 300 B.C. scribes started putting a sign for the gap, and the same sign was also used for the end of their sentences (⪝), which is similar to our period (.). This sign did not make the slightest difference to the computational results of their numerals, but simply eliminated the confusion as to whether there was a gap or not. They continued the operations on their numerals, with or without the sign for the gap, in exactly the same way, producing the same result. A few examples are, 3 6+12 = 318, and 306 + 12 = 318, or 3 6 x12 = 3672, and 306 x 12= 3672. However, it was a historically important step, being the first 'zero' in abstract symbol, albeit with limited function. The Babylonians could not use their zero independently outside the numerals, for example, as a product of computation: 6 - 6 = 0 because they did not consider the zero as a number like 1, 2, 3, 4 .... This limitation is understandable; as other numbers each have a real quantity which we can relate to any concrete object, for example, pebbles or fingers. There is no way the zero, without quantity, can be correlated to any object. The concept of the zero as an independent number, similar to 1, 2, 3, 4, 5, 6, 7, 8, 9, and subject to the same rules of operation as others numbers. is one the greatest intellectual achievement in all mathematics. This was achieved about 900 years after the Babylonians. Their zero only functioned as a sign for filling the gap in the place-value numerals, although they could compute with the zero, exactly as with the empty 'gap' in their numerals.

The Babylonians, however, extended the use of the zero by placing one or two zeroes at the end of the numerals, thus imaginatively expanding the role of the zero, for example, in 60 or 8200. By so doing they made an important contribution to mathematics. The Babylonians also used the zero at the beginning of the numerals before the sexagesimal fractions, which was invented 1300 years before its equivalent decimal point in decimal fractions.

"In a mathematical text from Susa," Georges Ifrah says "the scribe, obviously not knowing how to express the result of subtracting 20 from 20, concluded in this way: '20 minus 20....you see' (382). In another tablet with a problem of distribution of grain, the scribe wrote, "The grain is exhausted" (Ibid). Ifrah comments, "These two examples show that the notion of 'nothing' was not yet conceived as a number." In other words, they could not use their zero independently outside the numerals, for example, as a product of computation, as in 20 - 20 = 0.

Another limitation of the Babylonian numerals was the base of 60, which did not facilitate the memorization of their multiplication and division tables. Although 60 can be divided with advantage by 30, 20, 15, 10, 6, 5, 4, 3, 2, it does not compensate for the large base of 60. Furthermore, they used the base of 60 with the underlying base of ten below sixty. For example, Y <<YYY <<Y is (60X60x60) + (23x60) + 21 = 217, 401. The mixed base caused difficulty in large computations, particularly multiplication and division. No doubt because of these difficulties they prepared a large number of tables for multiplication, division, squares and square roots to speed calculations with large numbers. Furthermore, since they used only three separate symbols, for 1, 10, and the zero, they had to use the additive principle extensively. For example, our 9 is a separate symbol, but Babylonians had to use nine attached symbols of one, and for 50 they used five attached symbols of ten. In spite of these defects, the brilliant Babylonian numerals were incomparably superior to all other ancient numerals for computation until the seventh century A.D.

EGYPTIAN ARITHMETIC

Compared to the Babylonians' the Egyptians' arithmetic is much less efficient. Most of the information on Egyptian mathematics is documented in the Rhind Papyrus, now in the British Museum, and the Moscow Papyrus. They were written not in hieroglyphs but in cursive hieretic characters where partial cipherization took place. In Hieroglyphs the numbers were written in simple vertical lines representing one, and for numbers 2 to 9 they used the additive principle, for example, 3, \|\| Perfect cipherization requires an individual sign for each number, written with one stroke of the pen like our first ten numbers.

1, 2, 3, 4, 5, 6, 7, 8, 9, 10, 20, 30, 40, 50, 60, 70, 80, 90

100, 200, 300, 400,.........1000, 2000, 3000 ....6000.........9000....

The Egyptians used repeated addition for their multiplication rather than direct computations. They used unit fractions and developed the basic rules of calculation with them (Flegg, 131).

IX. GREEK ARITHMETIC

"Logistica," meaning calculation, is what the Greeks called what we today commonly refer to as "arithmetic." Arithmetic to them meant what is today the abstract study of numbers. The Greeks used their alphabet usually with a diacritical mark for their numbers, which is apparent also in the Ionian system, the best of all Greek systems.

α	β	γ	δ	ε	ϛ	ζ	η	θ	ι	κ	λ	μ	ν	ξ	ο	π	ϟ
1,	2,	3,	4,	5,	6,	7,	8,	9,	10,	20,	30,	40,	50,	60,	70,	80,	90

ρ	σ	τ	υ	φ	χ	ψ	ω	ϡ	,α	,β
100,	200,	300,	400,	500,	600,	700,	800,	900,	1,000,	2,000;

M (myriad) for 10,000; above M a multiplicative system was used, for example, $\overset{\nu}{M}$ = 50 x10000 = 50,000.

This is an additive as well as a multiplicative system. The Ionian numerals were only partially deciphered; the signs for the numbers are not unique but shared with their alphabet. The signs have separate diacritical marks, and often one or more numbers were put above others in a nonlinear fashion. Learning this system, writing it down, and computing relatively small amounts were not difficult. However, calculating with large numbers would have been very difficult. It is interesting to note that when large numbers were required, the Greek astronomers used the Babylonian system. Professor Boyer (q. by Flegg, 90), who has eloquently defended the deciphered Ionian system, thinks that "the introduction by the Egyptians of the idea of cipherization constitutes a decisive step in the development of numeration, and their contribution in this is every way comparable in significance to that of Babylonians in adopting the position principle." Undoubtedly, ciphered numbers are better than unciphered ones; however, with familiarity the Babylonian additive signs, TT ,TTTT , <<, <<<<, 2, 4, 20, or 40, respectively, could be recognized instantaneously. Although the Greek numerals could sometimes be arranged as in the place-value system, in many complicated calculations ciphered numerals would not be as efficient as the non-ciphered Babylonian place-value system. Archimedes invented a system of numerals with ten to the power eight, with which he could write very large numbers, and compute with them; however, hardly anyone used it because of its complexity. The best proof for the essential requirement of the place-value with a zero in a perfect system of numerals is that even a genius like Archimedes could not create satisfactory numerals without the place-value and the zero. Most mathematicians think that place-value is far more important than cipherization.

Greek mathematicians did not accept the Babylonian place-value system, but later Greek astronomers adopted it. They made several changes, which we see best in Ptolemy's (c.150 A.D.) famous book on astronomy, *Almagest*. Ptolemy's numerals incorporated at least three different systems, the Greek, the Egyptian, and the Babylonian (Pedersen, 49). "Ptolemy used the nonpositional decimal additive system, using Greek letters for whole numbers even when the number was more than sixty, whereas the Babylonians used the sexagesimal system consistently. Ptolemy replaced the few Babylonian symbols with large numbers of Greek alphabetic symbols, thus destroying the beautiful simplicity of the Babylonian system," says Pederson (52). He continues that "Ptolemy also used the Egyptian system of unit fractions, e.g., 2/23 = 1/12 + 1/276. Ptolemy used the Babylonian sexagesimal system only for fractions"(Ibid). "The Greeks brought inconsistency," according to Neugebauer, "which is still visible in modern astronomy;" Neugebauer continues, "it took about 2,000 years of migration of astronomical knowledge from Mesopotamia via Greeks, Hindus, and Arabs to arrive at a truly absurd numerical system." (17). Calculations were not easily performed in the sexagesimal system (Pedersen, 55). It was even more difficult in the mixed Greek system. The *Almagest* contains very large numbers of computation with numerals, often of intricate nature. "Even allowing for the greater speed made possible by auxiliary tables, and great familiarity with sexagesimal technique possessed by ancient astronomers," Pedersen writes, "one cannot help making the assumption that Ptolemy must have had assistants helping him with routine work in the numerical field." (56).

The Greek astronomers used their zero exactly like the Babylonians, only in the numerals, at the end of the numerals, and in the beginning of sexagesimal fractions. They never used an independent zero outside the numerals. During the first and second centuries, the Greek zero was written as ō , ō, (Neugebauer, 14), and in A.D. 467 the zero was ō . (Ifrah, 384). Only later, in the Byzantine manuscripts, was the zero written as o, which looked exactly like the Greek letter omicron, which was also used as 70 in the Greek numerals. We do not know when the symbol 'o' was first considered as the first letter of the Greek word *ouden* (nothing). Neugebauer (Ibid) asserts that the papyri do not support the idea of 'o' as ouden or nothing but, rather, suggests that it was an arbitrarily invented symbol intended to indicate an empty place exactly like the Babylonian separation mark (≹).

ROMAN NUMERALS: The practical minded Romans took many aspects of Greek civilization but ignored the Greek 'mathematica,' viewing it as of no practical value. Their numerical symbols were taken from the Etruscans. The symbols of their numbers to 49 were probably not taken from the alphabet but were basically variations of vertical lines grouped in tens, as in many other civilizations (Fig. 15). In certain situations they used the subtractive method, for example 9 as 10-1, IX. Computation using the Roman numerals was difficult, so they used the abacus extensively. Although their numerals were inefficient, because of their political power it was extensively used for millenia throughout Europe. Even now we occasionally use them on a clock face, on in chapters or sections of a book.

X. INDIAN ARITHMETIC

DECIMAL SYSTEM. As we have already discussed, the decimal system of counting in groups of ten probably began even before civilizations adapted it. The third oldest civilization in the Indus Valley in India (c. 2500 -1700 B.C.), evidences the use of a decimal system, a ruler with decimal divisions made from a shell having been found there (Flegg, 102). The only useful modification of this several-thousand-years-old decimal system is the binary system, consisting of one and the zero, "on" and "off" in the modern computer. The philosopher-mathematician Leibniz (1688) became mystical about it and thought of one as the God who created the universe out of the void of zero. For example:

Computer binary	1	10	11	100	101	110	111	1000	1001	1010
Indian numerals	1	2	3	4	5	6	7	8	9	10

The binary system is only practical if the user is capable of operating at extremely fast speed as in a computer otherwise it is much more efficient to use the Hindu-Arabic numerals. From time to time the suggestion is made that 12 would be a better unit than 10, since 12 can be divided by 2, 3, 4, and 6. The advantage is minor, if any, and not significant enough to replace the decimal system. Probably since the later part of the seventh, and certainly since the fourth century B.C., India had a system of numerals with separate signs for 1 through 9, and then signs for :

10 20 30 40 50 60 70 80 90 100....1000.....4000....etc.

INDIAN ARITHMETICAL SYMBOLS

The signs of the old Indian numerals most probably originated in the same location, Magadha, and at the same time, in the later part of seventh century B.C., as the Brahmi alphabet, which we have established in the first section of the book. It was a time and place of great creativity. Buddha was reputed to be highly proficient in arithmetic, particularly with large numbers. It is quite probable that the inventor of the Brahmi script, after designing individual abstract signs to each sound of the unwritten Sanskrit language, would also think of assigning different abstract signs to each of the numbers, carried orally for centuries. Only at the time of King Asoka (c. 250 B.C.) do we see numerous number symbols carved on the rocks, along with the Brahmi alphabet. The journey of the ten numerical symbols from India, through Bagdad, Spain and Italy, to all the countries of Europe and the world, is well documented. The symbols of Brahmi numbers modified through 2,250 years are shown below. Fig.16.

Asoka's (250B.C.)	—	=	≡	¥	h	ψ	2	S	?	
Bakhshali (650-700)	/	२	३	ऋ	21	ʎ	Ω	Z	?	•
Devanagari (since 900)	१	२	३	४	५	६	७	८	९	०
South India (c.1100)	⌒	T	3	ɤ	n	ᓴ	ʔ	7	∼	o
Arabic (since1100)	١	٢	٣	٤	٥	٦	٧	٨	٩	٠
Europe (since 1300)	1	2	3	4	5	6	7	8	9	0

The characteristics of these symbols is that from the beginning they were almost fully ciphered. This means that each symbol represents only a single number and nothing else, and each sign was written in only one stroke; and they were not shared by alphabet. At the beginning only 2, 3, and a few large numbers needed two or three strokes, but later the 2 and 3 were cipherized. There is a great advantage of ciphered numbers, particularly in calculations. The first nine symbols of these numbers gradually changed over the millenia and spread throughout the world. Our 1, 2, 3, 4, 5, 6, 7, 8, 9 originated from these ancient Indian symbols, and the 0 symbol was created in the seventh century A.D. in India. This set of symbols is perfect, enduring for over 2,300 years, the most widely known, and most extensively used of all mathematical symbols. "It has now become only real universal language"(Ifrah,459).

THE POSITION OR PLACE-VALUE SYSTEM

This system refers to the position of the digits within the numerals. It is based on the ideology that the value of a number depends on the position of each digit in the numerals; for example, because of the position of digits such as 321, 3 in hundreds, 2 in tens, and 1 in the units, it is a completely different number than 123, which contains the same digits. The place-value system was first invented by the Sumerians-Babylonians before 1,800 B.C. About 2,000 years later, three other civilizations also invented it independently, namely, the Indians, the Chinese and the Mayans (Ifrah, 432).

A poem written with much poetic imagination meshed with some facts, a few centuries after Gautama Buddha (c.566-486 B.C.), and based on his legendary life, *Lalitavistara* contains an interesting anecdote. Based on this, Sir Edwin Arnold composed a popular poem,*The Light of Asia*. In the story, Prince Dandapani wanted to give away his daughter in marriage to a youth worthy of her. As was the custom of that time among the royal societies, Prince Gautama and a few other princes competed to win Princess Gopa's hand. They were tested in archery, swordsmanship, and other physical and intellectual skills, including mathematics. Buddha was asked to name all the numbers above koti (ten million) in progression of hundreds, and he correctly answered *ayuta, niyuta, kankara, vivara, ksobbya, vivaba, utsanga, bahula, nagabala, titilambha, vyabasthana-prajnapti, hetuhila, karahu, hetvindriya, samaptalambha, ganagati, niravadyas, mudrabala, sarvabala, visamjnagati, sarvajna, vibhutangama*, to the *tallakshana* (10 to the power 53) was the first tower of numbers, and the highest one reached 10 to the power 421. (Datta and Singh v.1,10). "This number sequence was the work of one person with amazing logical and coherent structure," says Menninger (141).

Whether our good lord Buddha actually performed those feats cannot be ascertained on the evidence of the poem. However, he certainly won Princess Gopa's hand. We know from other evidence that both oral and, most probably, written arithmetic were available in the area where Buddha was born, and India had a long tradition of counting very large numbers. Aryabhatta's *Aryabhatiya* (499) contains in the *Ganitapada,* the names of the place-values in decimal system, from lower to higher,*"eka* (one),*dasa* (ten),*sata* (hundred), *sahasra* (thousand), *ayuta* (ten-thousand), *laksa* (hundred-thousand), *proyuta* (million), *koti* (ten-million) and *vrnda* (hundred-million) are from place to place each ten times the preceding."

'NAMED' PLACE-VALUE NUMERALS

Consider the structure of 'named' place-value numerals, where both the coefficient and the order of place are given. For example, 4537 could be rendered either *sapta tridasa pancasata catursahasra* or *catursahasra pancasata tridasa sapta* (respectively, seven thirty five-hundred four-thousand or four-thousand five-hundred thirty seven); the order was irrelevant.

Quoting from Roger Biillard's works on the Indian astronomers, Ifrah (445) says, "Earlier than A.D. 458, the first nine numerals of the ancient Brahmi numeration were, like the first nine ordinary Sanskrit number words, entirely adopted to the base of 10 and the place-value principle, so that the number 4769 was written either in the form [illegible] or this one *nava sat sapta catur* (9674)." (Ibid, 457). These word place-value numerals without zero are the first documented numerals of that type in India. However, their equivalent in abstract symbols did not appear that early; there is no known documentation of such progress. This is because Ifrah surprisingly does not see any useful difference between the two systems, the word numerals and the numerals in abstract symbols. Ifrah (451) says, "The difference between the two systems was merely a matter of graphic convention." However, Ifrah agrees with most other historians of mathematics that "the Gurjara deed of Shankhadeva engraved on the copperplate is regarded as the oldest known example of the Indian place-value numeration without a zero [in abstract symbols] (Ibid,437-38)." It is dated in *Ched* 346 (595 A.D.) and indicates the number 346 as follows, [illegible] (Ibid). *Therefore, far more developed Hindu-Arabic numerals including the '0' in abstract symbols could not have been created before 595* A.D.(see fig.17). Within a few years the place-value numerals in abstract symbols *without* the '0' spread to the Hinduized kingdoms of Cambodia in 604, and Champa

(South Vietnam) in 609 (Needham, v. 3, p.11), confirming the earlier appearance of this system of numerals in India.

We have already looked at the names of the place-value from *ayuta* to *tallaksana* above *koti* (ten million) in hundreds, and below *koti* in tens (decimal). For eample, *panca tridasa dwisata ekasahasra saptaprayuta* meaning five thirty two-hundred one-thousand seven-million, (7,001,235). If we write in the reversed order, for example, seven-million one-thousand two-hundred thirty five, the number is the same. The Indians wrote them in both directions. This type of numerals is called 'named' place-value numerals because the units of place-values are named. Thus the idea of place-value in India is very old, at least as old as *Lalitavistara* (c.100 B.C.). In 'named' place-value numerals there was no need of a zero (*sunya*). However, when the names of the place-value units were abandoned, leaving only the coefficients, zero became essential in the place-value word numerals. Take the example of the earlier numerals: *sapta sunya gagana eka dwi tri panca* (seven zero zero one two three five) could not be written without zeroes. Destitute of the distinctiveness of the name of the order of place, the strict order of recital became crucial. Directly developed from the 'named' place-value numerals, these types of numerals are called "decimal word place-value numerals with zero." In turn, the Hindu-Arabic numerals in abstract symbols evolved from them.

Starting in the fifth century A.D., Indian mathematician-astronomers experimented with many types of numerals. They manipulated these numerals in a variety of aspects, almost all in verse, in words or alphabet, left to right or right to left orientation, place-value, and with or without the zero (*sunya*). Versified mathematics required word or alphabetic numbers; to ensure harmony in the meter of the verse, there were a dozen or more names for each number. For example, six could be written as *Anga sarvedanga*, (an Indian work which had six parts), *Rtu* (season, of which India had six), *Rasa* (for the six elements of taste, such as sour, sweet, etc.), *Kamarbadan* (for the six-faced god of war), and *Tarka* (representing the six types of reasoning). Zero was written as *sunya*, (empty), *akash, gagana, byom, ambar* (sky), *puskar* (water, lotus), *abhab* (absence) and many other ways. There were also words like one, two, three, and four, as well as abstract numbers,1, 2, 3, 4...

Eka	*dvi*	*tri*	*catur*	*panca*	*sat*	*sapta*	*asta*	*nava*	*sunya*
1	2	3	4	5	6	7	8	9	no symbol

Of course, the abstract symbols could not be used in verse.

WORD *versus* ABSTRACT NUMBER SYMBOLS IN NUMERALS.

There is significant misunderstanding among many historians of Indian mathematics concerning the word numerals, and numerals in abstract symbols (old Indian abstract numerals and the Hindu-Arabic numerals). For example, Ifrah emphasizes, "Thus the essence of a decimal numeration with the same structure as ours is independent of its symbolization. The nature of the symbols chosen (graphic signs without direct visual reference, letters of an alphabet, words with or without evocative meanings etc.) does not matter provided they are never ambiguous (p.451)." Georges Ifrah, who has written the best researched book on this subject, made a major mistake here, like many other historians of Indian mathematics, causing much confusion. In fact, there is a fundamental difference between the two. The versed Indian word or alphabetic numerals, with multiple names for each number, has ineffective presentation and virtually no computational ability. Conversely, the same numerals in abstract symbols, the Hindu-Arabic, possess both efficient presentation and an intrinsically elegant method of computation. Although the Hindu numerals developed from the word numerals with place-value and the zero, as we will show later it took over 170 years for this improvement. Consider the following example, from Bhaskara I (629 A.D.) given by Ifrah (p.447-448).

viyadambarakasasasynyayamaramaveda

sky/atmosphere/space/void/primordial couple/Rama/Veda

0 0 0 0 2 3 4

In ascending order of powers ten in right to left direction the number is 4,320,000 in Hindu numerals. This mistake of thinking that the versed word numerals are just equal to the numerals in abstract symbols has caused many errors. Ifrah (450) also mistakenly says that Aryabhatta (499) in the early sixth century knew the Indian numerals and the zero sign as well as the symbolic number word.

Roger Billard (quoted by Ifrah,452), says "The symbolic number words [in verse] have been accurately preserved through time and many handwritten copies. This preservation is all the more striking because Indian manuscripts are never very old, physically speaking: our copies of them were usually made no more than two or three centuries ago." Billard continues, "Numerical data recorded in [abstract] numerals would surely have come down to us in an unusable state"(Ibid). In fact, no numerals in abstract symbols came to us from the fifth, sixth, or seventh centuries or earlier manuscripts or their reliable copies. This is the reason why the historians have to depend on abstract numerals carved on the rocks or copperplate deeds. Fortunately, many of them are available with dates in the Indian era. *The Bakhshali manuscript*, an exception, will be discussed later.

Based on the ancient Indian phonetics, Aryabhatta (499) created a complicated alphabetic numerals and divided the consonants into*Vargas* and *Avarga* alphabet. The vowel 'a' is used for units and powers of ten, the vowel 'i' for hundreds and thousands, 'u' for ten-thousands and hundred-thousands, until the power of 17, then it could be repeated for even higher powers. In this system he could name the numbers, out of order, in the numerals to fit the meter of the verse. These alphabetic verse numerals are extremely complicated, and hardly anyone used them after him. Ifrah says (450) that Aryabhatta "uses a decimal base, place-value principle, nine numerals, and a tenth sign that functions as a zero." Aryabhatta, of course, was aware of the place-value **word** numerals with zero in the *Lokabivaga* (458 A.D.) but not the Hindu numerals in abstract symbols. The manuscript *Aryabhatiya* (499) certainly does not contain the Hindu numerals in abstract symbols. Furthermore, even numerals with place-value *without* zero in abstract symbols did not develop until 595 A.D. as Ifrah and other scholars agree. Aryabhatta also gave the rules in verse for extracting square and cube roots which are similar to those one we use today. However, his commentator Bhaskara,1, (629 A.D.), [not the great Bhaskara (1150)], a minor mathematician, simplified and improved Aryabhatta's numerals in the alphabet in this form: k, t, p, or y for *one*; kh, th, ph, or r for *two*; g, d, b, or l, for *three*; gha, dha, bh, or v for *four*; n, n, m, or s for *five*; c, t or s, for *six*; ch, th, or s for *seven*; j,d or h, for *eight;* jh or dh, for *nine*, and n, n, and vowels for *sunya.* Each of the alternative letters were used for the specific number to fit the meter of the verse. Bhaskara,1, used alphabetic and word numerals with decimal place-value and the zero, and not the Hindu numerals in abstract symbols as Ifrah mistakenly claims."The [abstract] symbol is not a mere formality," says Dantzig, "it is the very essence of algebra" (80). This is also true for abstract arithmetical symbols.

There is a vast difference between the ideas, however clear, which can be used only to a limited extent; and the same ideas with appropriate symbols are used extensively in mathematics. For example, Archimedes (287-212 B.C.) had the basic idea of integral calculus in his theory of exhaustion, but he could not discover integral calculus without proper symbols. Newton (1642-1727) and Leibniz (1646-1716) had to discover the abstract symbols and new methods to develop calculus. Also Appollonius (260-190 B.C.) in his conic sections had a good grasp of analytic geometry, but it needed abstract symbols, and the algebraic method deviced by Descartes (1596-1650) and Fermat(1601-1665). Similarly, many Indian mathematicians, since 458 A.D. used decimal numerals with place-value and *sunya* in words. However, they could not discover adequate abstract symbols, although available to create the Hindu numerals, except for the *sunya* which could be used in arithmetic. In the history of mathematics, these types of major improvements take centuries and always need mathematical geniuses.

Datta, an authority on the Hindu mathematics, writes that, "The Hindu alphabetic system, unlike these employed by the Greeks and the Arabs, was never used by common people, or for the purpose of making calculations; their knowledge was strictly confined to the learned and their use to the expression of numbers in verse" (Datta & Singh, v.1, p. 64). This is equally true for the word numerals. During this period calculations were done with old Indian numerals in abstract symbols without place-value and the zero. Without calculation there is no arithmetic. If the alphabetic or word numerals were not used in computation, how could we call them arithmetical numbers?

PLACE-VALUE NUMERALS WITH *SUNYA* (ZERO) IN WORDS

A profound concept like the zero as a number can be created only by a great mathematical genius. It also needed the contributions of large number of creative minds, in different fields, over the centuries. In Sanskrit, *sunya* means nothing, empty, void, absence, sky, and other related things and ideas. *Sunya* was used in 300 B. C. by Kautilya, the Machiavellian minister of Emperor Chandragupta. In his book on politics and power, *Arthashastra*, he mentioned *sunya* in several places, such as referring to no guard - that is, the absence of guard - at the royal palace as *sunyapal.* The poet Pingala used *sunya* around 200 B.C.; a century later the nihilistic Buddhist philosopher Nagarjuna wrote a book on *sunyavada*, the philosophy of nothingness.

The Jainas are the followers of Mahavira, a contemporary of Buddha. Many of them still live in western India. They made significant contribution to mathematics. One of their works *Lokavibhaga,* dated 458 A.D., contains decimal place-value numerals with zeroes, but in words and in a right-to-left direction, for example, five voids-two-seven-sky-one-three (0-0-0-0-0-2-7-0-1-3), equivalent to our 3,107,200,000. This is the first documented place-value numerals with zeroes in *words.* During the fertile period of Indian mathematics, from Aryabhatta's *Aryabhatiya* (499) to Brahmagupta's *Siddhanta* (628), several mathematicians contributed to the concept of the zero and the place-value numerals.

In Varahamihira's *Panca-Siddhantika* (505 A.D.),*sunya* (zero) was mentioned several times: "*Thirty six increased by two, three, nine, twelve, nine, three, sunya (zero) are the days*" (xviii, 35). Vararamihira was the first mathematician who used an independent zero (in words) for increase (addition) and decrease (subtraction). However, he failed to give the results on these operations. We know from the elementary school days that without memorizing the results of addition, subtraction, multiplication and division on the numbers like 1,2,3,4,5,6,7,8,9, *et cetera*, arithmetical calculations are impossible. The results are not automatically known but must be learned. Exactly the same rules apply to the '0' as a number, which cannot be used properly unless we know the results of their operations as given by a mathematician. Furthermore, Varahamihira did not discover an abstract symbol for the *sunya.* "The operation of addition and subtraction are incidentally mentioned in *Panca-siddhantika* of Varahamihira," says Datta and Singh (239). Datta's remark that Varahamihira *incidentally* mentioned the two rules of operation on the zero without results suggest that Varahamihira was not aware that he was at the juncture of one of the greatest inventions in mathematics. Thus, Varahamihira failed to make his *sunya* a number suitable for arithmetical calculations. In spite of all these limitations he advanced the concept of the independent zero more than anyone before Brahmagupta.

Siddhasena Gani, a contemporary of Varahamihira, stated in a problem of square root extraction: "*Half of the eight zeroes are four zeroes*" (Datta and Singh, v. i, 79). Jinabhadra Gani (529-589) wrote, "*Twenty-two forty-four, eight zeroes* (224,400,000,000). Elsewhere he describes "*Two hundred thousand forty-one thousand nine hundred and sixty; removing (apavartana) the zeroes, the numerator is four-zero-seven-one-five, and the denominator four-eight-three-nine-two" (Ibid).* In these examples, the mathematicians used the decimal position value with the zero in word numerals. Verse and words, the bane in Indian mathematics, delayed its development, particularly of abstract symbols. Indians' contribution at that time, other than of Varahamihira's, was the use of large numbers of zeroes at the end of the numerals in words.

DEVELOPMENT OF INDEPENDENT ZERO IN WORD & ABSTRACT SYMBOL

The Babylonian, Greek, and the Indian *sunya* (zero) during this period were used *only* in the numerals, as gap-holders in a place-value system, and were limited in function. In contrast, today '0' is used in the numerals as well as outside the numerals, for example, as a result of computation, 20 - 20 = 0.

"If we knew history better," said Emile Male, "we would find a great intelligence at the origin of every innovation" (Ifrah,428). If that is so, two of the greatest inventions in mathematics, namely, the modern zero as a number and the Hindu-Arabic numerals, certainly required a very great genius in mathematics indeed.

The third component of our numeral system, and by far the most important, is the zero. As the zero is unique in having no quantity it needs an abstract symbol as well as the rules of operation like 1, 2, 3,....or a, b, c,.... to be in the same class. Ifrah says (459) "The zero originally meant void, an empty column in the counting board. When and how did it become enriched by acquiring the meaning of "nothing," as in "10-10"? The question is one of the most interesting in the history of science, but unfortunately we cannot answer it in the present state of our knowledge."

Brahmagupta's rule, one among many others (sec. II, *19), states, "The sum of affirmative and negative, if they are equal, is naught." This statement has the most profound implications. This means 10 + (-10) = 0, or x + (-x) = 0. Here, for the first time in history, *a zero meaning "nothing" existed independently as a product of computation, and outside the numerals.* So Brahmagupta's zeroes were not only space-holders in a place-value system. However, Brahmagupta's zero (*sunya*) was expressed in word and not in abstract symbol; as such it was unsuitable for calculations. We will show later that Brahmagupta replaced the *sunya* by an abstract symbol "0" borrowed from the redundant old Indian symbol for 20. Thus, Brahmagupta's '0' means 'nothing,' has an abstract symbol and rules of operation as all numbers must have to be useful in arithmetic and other branches of mathematics. As we have already noticed, before Brahmagupta, the zeroes of the Babylonians, Greeks or the Indians, were not numbers, only space-holders in the place-value system, Brahmagupta freed the numbers zeroes from the numerals; thus, almost all branches of mathematics could use the freed zero, with its rules of operation just like our present day zero. This was a radical departure for mathematics, which was primarily concerned with quantity or magnitude and related ideas.

In *Brahma-Sphuta-Siddhanta* (628), Brahmagupta stated the rules of operation for the positive numbers, zero, and the negative numbers simultaneously in Sanskrit verse. (Trs. by H.T. Colebrook, Section 2, p.339, and modern symbols by the author). Affirmative means positive, and naught or cipher is zero. Negative numbers are discussed in another chapter. Brahmagupta' rules are as follows:

"Section II p.339, 31. Rule for addition of affirmative and negative quantities and cipher: *19. The sum of two affirmative quantities is affirmative* (a)+(b) = (a+b); *of two negative is negative* (-a) + (-b) = - (a+b); *of an affirmative and a negative is their difference* (a) + (-b) = (a) - (+b); *or, if they are equal, nought,* (a) + (-a) = (0).*The sum of cipher and negative is negative* (0) + (-a) = (- a); *of affirmative and nought is positive,* (a) + (0) = (a)*; of two cipher is cipher* (0) + (0) = (0)."

*"#32-33.Rules for subtraction: *20-21. Negative, taken from cipher, becomes positive,* (0) - (-a) = (a); *and affirmative becomes negative,* (0) - (a) = (-a); *Negative, less cipher is negative* (- a) - (0) = (-a); *positive, is positive* (a) - (0) = (a); *cipher, naught* (0) - (0) = (0)." *"#34. Rules for multiplication: *22. The product of a negative quantity and an affirmative is negative* (-a) (b) = (-ab) ; *of two negatives, is positive* (-a) (-b) = ab; *of two affirmatives, is affirmative* (a) x (b) = (ab). *The product of cipher and negative* (0) x (-a) = (0), *or of cipher and affirmative, is nought* (0) x (a) = (0); *of two ciphers, is cipher* (0) x (0) = (0)."

*"#35-36. Rules for division: *23-24. Positive, divided by positive, or negative by negative, is affirmative* (-a) / (-b) = (a/b); *cipher, divided by cipher, is nought* (0)/(0) = (0). *Positive, divided by negative, is negative* a/(-b) = (-a/b). *Negative, divided by affirmative is negative* (-a) / (b) = (a/b). *Positive, or negative, divided by cipher, is a fraction with that for denominator (Tach-ch'heda,* having that for denominator: having in this instance, cipher for denominator, to a finite quantity for numerator)." [Author's note: we are not sure what he meant, however, "the Hindus did not recognize the operation of division by zero as valid in arithmetic;" says Datta quoting Narayana (v. I, 239). Even today we consider the result of division by the zero as *undefined.* "But the division of zero by a number was recognized as valid." "*or cipher divided by negative* (0)/(-a) = (0) *or affirmative* (0)/(a) = (0)."

*"Rules for involution and evolution: *24. The square of negative,* (-a) (-a) = + (aa) *and affirmative is positive* (a) (a) = + (aa); *of cipher, is cipher, cube is cipher ; square root is cipher, (#35) cube root is cipher."*

Here we see extensive use of independent zeroes in different mathematical situations. Brahmagupta was the first mathematician in the world who consciously and deliberately gave the rules of operations on the zero as all other types of numbers have. Obviously, this was based on his clear conception of the zero as a number like 1, 2, 3, 4, 5, 6,7, 8, 9,....x, y, z. Brahmagupta gave his zero the rules of operation with which it gained independence to function with any other number in mathematics rather than only be confined within the numerals. Brahmagupta, however, composed his *Samhita* in verse; he could not avoid a long pernicious tradition. During this period each of the old Indian numbers had several names in words or letters of the alphabet, but each of them also had an individual abstract symbol. As *sunya* was not considered a number before this period, there was no abstract symbol for it. However, after giving all the rules of operation on the *sunya*, Brahmagupta realized that his new number needed an abstract symbol as did all other numbers. Furthermore, when he tried to calculate with his *sunya*, and the *rnatmak* (negative) numbers, he realized that the Indians rarely used word numbers for calculations, as they were too inefficient. Naturally, for the *sunya* he searched the symbols in the old Indian numerals. As the new Hindu numerals needed only ten symbols, he used the first nine symbols from 1 through 9, from the old Indian abstract numerals, and looked at the redundant symbols for his *sunya*. Wisely, he avoided the number used for ten (∝), which might have caused confusion between the old 10 and the new 0. The next number symbol was for twenty (0). He took the symbol 0 for his *sunya*, and thus created our 0 in symbol. Brahmagupta's 0 had all the properties to function as a number and could be used in almost all branches of mathematics. Halstead remarked on the zero:

> The importance of the creation of the zero mark can never be exaggerated. This giving to airy nothing, not merely a local habitation and a name, a picture, a symbol, but helpful power, is characteristic of the Hindu race whence it sprang. It is like coining *Nirvana* into dynamos. No single mathematical creation has been more potent for the general on-go of intelligence and power (20).

Brahmagupta was the director of the famous astronomical laboratory in the capital city of Ujjain, made famous by the great poet and dramatist Kalidasa. When he was thirty, in 628 A.D., Brahmagupta published his magnum opus, *Brahma-Sphuta-Samhita*. A proud and arrogant Brahmin, highly unorthodox, he severely criticized even his great predecessor Aryabhatta, who had lived a hundred years earlier. The Persian scholar Alberuni, who lived in India for eleven years, wrote in Arabic a well-known book about India. In it he stated that Brahmagupta was "blind to the works of Aryabhatta because of hatred and was rude enough to compare Aryabhatta to a worm eating the wood, by chance describes certain character in [his book] without understanding them" (Linn, 48). This type of virulent remark about a scholar who should have been a revered *guru* made Brahmagupta highly unpopular. However, Brahmagupta mellowed with age, and at the age of 67 he wrote a book on astronomy in which he was very respectful to Aryabhatta.

We have already seen that Brahmagupta was incomparably more interested, and did more original work on the 'zero' as a number, than all other mathematicians before him. It is natural that he would search, and would be the discoverer of the abstract symbol '0' for his *sunya*. Brahmagupta's number "0," however, was a difficult concept. It spread slowly and spearingly; at first to China in Ch'in Chiu Shao's work in 1247, and first in Europoe in Harriot's (b.1560). Both of them put the '0' on one side of the equation as Brahmagupta did in words in 628 A.D.

This is probably the most useful, subtle and sophisticated achievement in mathematics, appealing to the intellect but not to the senses, easily useable and probably the most irreplaceable of all mathematical entities. Brahmagupta created, as it were, the very soul of mathematics, and there is nothing else equivalent to it. The importance of the zero (*sunya*) is stated by Tobius Dantzig:

> The Indian *sunya* was destined to become the turning point in a development without which the progress of modern science, industry or commerce is inconceivable. And the influence of this great discovery was by no means confined to arithmetic. By paving the way to a generalized number concept, it played as fundamental a role in practically every branch of mathematics. In the history of culture, the discovery of zero will always stand out as one of the greatest single achievements of human race. (35)

The '0' in the numerals was not as difficult a concept as the number "0." So this symbol spread to the Hinduized kingdom of Sumatra in 683 A.D., carved on the rock, with the date in the Indian Saka era 606 (৬০৬), confirming its appearance in India.

THE CREATION OF THE HINDU-ARABIC NUMERALS

We have already seen that since 458 A.D. many Indian mathematicians used word numerals in decimal place-value with the *sunya*. Only India produced word numerals of this type (Ifrah,446). We also know that all Indian mathematicians calculated with the old Indian numerals in abstract symbols without place-value or zero on dust boards. After discovering the abstract symbol for the *sunya* (0), Brahmagupta took the great final step by replacing the place-value word numerals with the zero by the abstract old Indian symbols from 1 to 9 as well as with his newly discovered symbol '0.' Thus, he created the Hindu-Arabic numerals. From 458 A.D., when the word numerals with place-value and *sunya* appeared in the *Lokavibhaga*, over 170 years earlier, none of the many Indian mathematicians could change the word numerals in abstract symbols. This was because they failed to reject the tradition of verse in words or alphabet; and none of them even tried to create an abstract symbol for the *sunya* as it was not considered a number like 1, 2, 3, 4, 5, 6,....

There are other unlikely possibilities. We have already mentioned that by 595 A.D. the decimal place-value, in abstract symbols without a zero, developed in India. It is unlikely that Brahmagupta arranged the numbers in a decimal place-value system in abstract symbols and placed his zero (0) in it where it was required. Sir Joseph Needham states it beautifully: "The Indian zero was like a garland thrown around the empty space on the counting board." (v.3 p.9). However, it is extremely difficult to prove that the Indians used a counting board. Furthermore, India never used a place-value numerals in abstract symbols with gaps for the zeroes. Only early Babylonians and the Chinese had gaps in their numerals. Indian place-value developed from the 'named' place-value system where they could avoid the use of the *sunya*. Another possibility is that Brahmagupta took the Babylonian sexagesimal or the Greek astro-nomers' mixed decimal-sexagesimal numerals, and converted them into consistant decimal numerals; that would have been the most difficult one as the mixed system is still used today in astronomy.

Why couldn't the mathematicians before Brahmagupta invent the ideal numerals when many of them had knowledge of all the components? The Babylonians failed to reject their sexagesimal system above sixty, and extend their decimal system to their entire numerals as well as create ciphered symbols. The Greek mathematicians failed to accept the Babylonian place-value and the zero for their numerals. The Greek astronomers took the place-value and the zero, but could not delete their sexagesimal system in their sexagesimal fraction, nor were they able to cipherize their numbers. The Indians went on the wrong track of mixing mathematics with verse where only words and alphabetic letters could be used, although abstract signs except for the zero were available in the old Indian numerals.

With these drastic changes the unorthodox genius Brahmagupta broke out of the Indian tradition of alphabetic and word numerals. The abstract symbol '0' as well as Hindu-Arabic numerals were undoubtedly created when Brahmagupta was at the height of his creative genius, just after 628. Most scholars who think that the Hindu numerals were created in the fifth or sixth century, or before Brahmagupta's *Samhita* (628), mistakenly think that the decimal place-value **word** numerals with a *sunya* are another way of expressing the Hindu-Arabic numerals (always in abstract symbols), and are equal in mathematical value. However, we have already shown that there is a fundamental difference between the two. Others based their belief on the unreliable date of the *Bakhshali manuscript,* which will be discussed later. There is no evidence that the denotation of Hindu numerals in abstract symbols developed before 629 A.D.

The Hindu numerals and the number '0' could be invented only by a great mathematical genius. Brahmagupta was the first mathematician who provided all the rules of operation on the zero in words. He also clearly stated the rules of addition, subtraction, multiplication, and division on the negative numbers. Furthermore, he made great contributions to algebra (Pell's equation and others), and geometry (trapezium). Surely he had the genius to create the Hindu-Arabic numerals as well as the modern zero. Moreover, there was even not a single mediocre mathematician between Brahmagupta's *Samhita* (628) and the Syrian Sebokht's writing (662) in India, Southeast Asia, China, Greece or Arabia.

The first document of the Hindu numerals did not come from India, but from Syria, 2,500 miles northwest of Ujjain, the center of Indian mathematics. Severus Sebokht was a bishop in the convent of Kenneshre on the Euphrates River, "which became the chief center of Greek learning in the Middle East during the seventh century" (Smith, I, 166). Sebokht was probably the most learned scholar in Greek and Babylonian mathematics and astronomy during that period in Asia and Europe. Ujjain and Kenneshre were probably the two leading centers of mathematics in the world at that time. It is expected that the mathematicians would travel from one center to the other to teach and learn. Sebokht wrote (Smith,v.1, 166) in 662 :

> I shall now speak of the knowledge of the Hindus....discoveries even more ingenious than those of the Greeks and Babylonians- their method of calculation which no words can praise strongly enough - I mean the system of nine symbols. If these things were known by the people who think that they alone have mastered the science because they speak Greek, they would perhaps be convinced though a little late in the day, that other folks, not only Greeks but men of a different tongue, know something as well as they.

The Syrian astronomer Sebokht was well versed in the Babylonian place-value numerals with the zero in the sexagesimal system, and he used in his astronomical works Ptolemy's Greek adaptation of the Babylonian numerals. Sebokht commented on the great superiority of the Hindu numerals particularly *in their method of calculation* over the Babylonians' and Ptolemy's numerals; there is no doubt that he was referring to the Hindu-Arabic numerals with the abstract symbol for the zero; since no numerals in history is superior to the Babylonians or Ptolemy's except the Hindu-Arabic numerals with the 0. Any numerals with nine symbols without a zero would be as primitive as the Indian numerals that existed in 595 A.D. As we have already seen, the Hindu numerals are much superior to the Babylonian or Ptolemy's numerals in every way. But why did Sebokht mention only nine symbols? Because the 0 was considered to be a sign and not a number by the majority of mathematicians for over 900 years. We will provide further examples later. Unfortunately, Sebokht in his enthusiasm forgot to mention the sign 0.

Two decades after the Syrian scholar's writings, we find the Indian numerals with the zero in abstract symbols in the Hindu Kingdoms of Cambodia in 683 A.D. (605 [illegible]) and in Sumatra in 683 A.D. (606 [illegible]). Carved on the rocks, the Hindu numerals confirmed Sebokht's observation. Syria is 2,500 miles northwest of Ujjain, India, and the Hindu kingdom of Sumatra is on the opposite side of India, 2,800 miles away from Ujjain. Within a few decades of the creation of the numerals in India, they spread to enormous distances. This is undoubtedly because the Indian traders, priests, and government officials traveled frequently, and often settled in these Hindu kingdoms of southeast Asian countries, to which they contributed all aspects of Indian culture. Both India and the southeast Asian countries used the old Indian numerals without place-value and the zero in abstract symbols, as well as the Indian word numerals, until the Hindu numerals were invented. Thus the transmission of Hindu numerals to the

Southeast Asian countries would only have taken a few years or decades, since India and the Southeast Asian countries were in the same cultural zone. We will discuss this in the chapter on the transmission of mathematics.

The Indians and the Southeast Asians knew the first nine arithmetical symbols of the old Indian numerals and only had to learn the symbol for the zero. Of course, they had to learn the new method of calculation with the zero making computation much faster and more efficient. The Hindu numerals, with the most advanced method of computation, including the use of a significant new number, the zero, were taken to China by Gautama Siddhartha (Chii-t'an Hsi-ta), the president of the Chinese astronomical board and the most famous of the Indian astronomers who were monopolizing the observatories of China during the T'ang dynasty (Schafer, 128). Siddhartha published an almanac in 718 A.D. which contains a section on the *Indian methods of calculation with nine numbers* (the same nine numbers to which Sebokht referred). "Whenever there is an empty space in a column (i.e. a zero)," Needham writes, "a dot is always placed" (12). This was undoubtedly the Hindu numerals of Sebokht (662), the Cambodians (683), and the Sumatrans (683). In the *Bakshali manuscript*, the Hindu numerals may be dated at the middle or later part of the seventh century written in this form, ৪... (4 ,000). The fist evidence of Hindu numerals in abstract symbols, ٤· (60) in India with a date is seen in Shahpur in a stone image inscription of Adityasena, Biharsharif, dated 672 A.D. (Mukherjee, 56). An inscription was discovered dated 875 A.D. at Gwalior, India containing 50 and 270 numerals.

Kushyar b. Labban (c. 970) wrote the book *Principles of Hindu Reckoning : on Understanding the Form of Nine Numerals.* He mentioned the symbols from 1 to 9, and later he explained the place value system. Then he advised placing the zero "where there is no number" (Berggren, 31). The greatest mathematician of Medieval Europe, Fibonacci of Pisa, whose book *Liber Abaci* (1202) was a landmark in the history of mathematics, opens with the statement, "I was introduced by a magnificent teacher to the art of reckoning with the nine Indian numerals....The numerals are 987654321" (Struik, 2/1). He stopped at nine symbols, just like the Syrian scholar five centuries earlier. However, Fibonacci later stated that with those nine numerals "and the sign of 0 which is called cipher, any desired number can be written" (Ibid). Obviously, Sebokht, like Siddhartha, Kushyar and Fibonacci, was speaking of the Hindu numeral system with nine symbols and the sign for the 0.

From the evidence in India, Syria, Cambodia, Sumatra, China, Arabia and Italy, we can conclude that our numeral system, with all the three components, the decimal base, the place-value, and the zero in abstract symbols, was invented between 629 A.D. and Sebokht's writing (662), this is confirmed by the Cambodians and Sumatrans in 683 A.D. Furthermore, we have already seen that Brahmagupta was at the height of his genius when he published the *Brahma-sphuta-samhita* in 628 A.D. The '0' and the Hindu-Arabic numerals were most probably invented soon after the *Samhita*, around 630 A.D.

The *Bakhshali Manuscript*, a collection from the works of several anonymous mathematicians probably over several centuries (similar to the Chinese collection, *Nine Chapters of Mathematical Arts*), contains the Hindu numerals with the zero symbol, a large dot (●). The manuscript dates around 900 A.D., and the mathematical content has been dated by different historians between 200 and 900 A.D. Recently, Indian historians of mathematics placed the content between the fourth and the seventh centuries (Gupta, 23). Takao Hayashi (1985), in his extensive study on *The Bakhshali Manuscript*, suggests the seventh century as the date of the work. The portions containing the Hindu numerals could not be dated before 629. None of the mathematicians, from the author of *Lokavibhaga* (458) through Aryabhatta (499) and Brahmagupta (628) mentioned the Hindu-Arabic numerals in abstract symbols. Therefore, the Hindu numerals in the *Bakhshali Manuscript* appeared after 629, perhaps in the later half of the seventh century. Sridhara, a minor mathematician lived between the seventh and ninth centuries (Gupta, 23). These dates are highly controversial, and probably none of these mathematicians were active during this period (629-662). It is interesting to note that many mathematicians wrote place-value numerals with *sunya* in words or alphabet since 458 A.D.; Brahmagupta, however, did not do so as he created superior abstract Hindu-Arabic numerals as well as the 0.

To think that the Hindu numerals and the number '0' developed without the involvement of a genius would be ridiculous, and at that time the only great mathematician was Brahmagupta; the more important evidence is his intense interest in the zero which we have already seen.

Many great inventions in retrospect look easy. If the creation of the Hindu numerals was not a difficult invention, why did not the Babylonians, Greek astronomers and, particularly, the Indian mathematicians before Brahhagupta discover them? Many of them had the knowledge of the decimal system, the place-value, the zero, and numbers in abstract symbols. Moreover, why did no mathematician invent the Hindu-Arabic numerals by changing the Babylonian place-value sexagesimal system to the decimal system? The Greeks and pre-Brahmagupta Indians were familiar with both systems. The modern astronomical notation is a mixture of sexagesimal and decimal systems, yet nobody changed it to a consistant decimal system. Neugebauer comments "It took 2000 years of migration of astronomical knowledge from the Mesopotamia via Greeks, Hindus, and Arabs to arrive at a truely absurd numerical system" (17).

Brahmagupta almost certainly created the Hindu numerals, and their operations after trials and errors, computing on the smooth surface of the sand-covered ground. After he invented our numerals, it was unlikely that he ever wrote them down on a birch bark or a palm leaf; even if he did, that would have disappeared long ago. It is much more likely that he explained the numerals, and their method of calculation, to his disciples on the dust table, as a teacher does on the chalkboard today. *Dhuli-karma* means working with the dust, and Brahmagupta was an enthusiastic proponent of the *dhuli-karma*. Even in his masterpiece *Brahma-Sphuta-Samhita*, he wrote, "Those who do not use *dhuli-karma* will get a bad reputation and their fame will not last" (Chapter VII, verse, 67, see also verse 62). For thousands of years India had a strong tradition of transmitting knowledge orally. Thus did Brahmagupta transmit knowledge of his numerals, a knowledge that others transmitted after him. Furthermore, as Billard says, "Numerical data recorded in [abstract] numerals would surely come down to us in a unusable state" quoted by Ifrah (452). During the last 13 centuries, the name and the time of the inventor has been lost. Hardly anyone learns numerals and their operations from a text, rather they learn from the parents or the teachers. This is as true today as it was 1,365 years earlier, only the sand table has been replaced by the chalkboard or paper.

Several mathematicians (Meninger, 399) have suggested that the large Indian oval zero, 0, was taken from the Greek small round zero, o. Why would Brahmagupta take only one symbol from a foreign source, when he already had taken the first nine old Indian symbols, and had at his disposal at least fifteen redundant old Indian symbols, familiar to him. There is nothing sacrosanct about the shape of 0. He could have selected the symbol for 40 (X) or 80 ([symbol]). Any of them would have served as well as our zero, 0. Furthermore, the Greek zero was [symbol], [symbol], [symbol], [symbol] in the first century A.D., after 109 A.D., second century, and in 467 A.D., respectively (Ifrah, 384). Only during the Byzantine empire did it change to 'o' probably too late to reach Brahmagupta. Professor Boyer (240) says about the Indian 0 that "It once was assumed that the round form stemmed originally from the Greek letter omicron,....but recent investigations seem to belie such an origin." One may consult Datta and Singh, Smith and

Karpinsky, Ifrah and other books on the Indian arithmetical symbols.

It is surprising that we find the symbols for the zero as 0 or a dot (•). Brahmagupta almost certainly did not invent a second sign, the dot (•) for the *sunya.* He used a dot sign for negative numbers, and it was always placed above the negative number. Some mathematicians think that the linear dot came from the sixth century poet Subandhu who mentioned that "the stars shone forth,...like zero dots,...scattered in the sky...(Flegg, 111). However, "like zero dots" in poetry does not make it a number. Probably, some later mathematician wanted a different look for the 0, and took the dot from Subandhu or some other source. We find it in the *Bakhshali Manuscript*, and in Cambodia carved on a rock with a date 683 A.D. Alternative words for the same number were frequently used in India, perhaps they extended this tradition even to the abstract symbol for the zero. The Arabs used a dot for the zero, the Chinese used a dot in the eighth century but a circle in the thirteenth century.

Fig. 17. ORIGIN OF NUMBER "0" AND HINDU-ARABIC NUMERALS

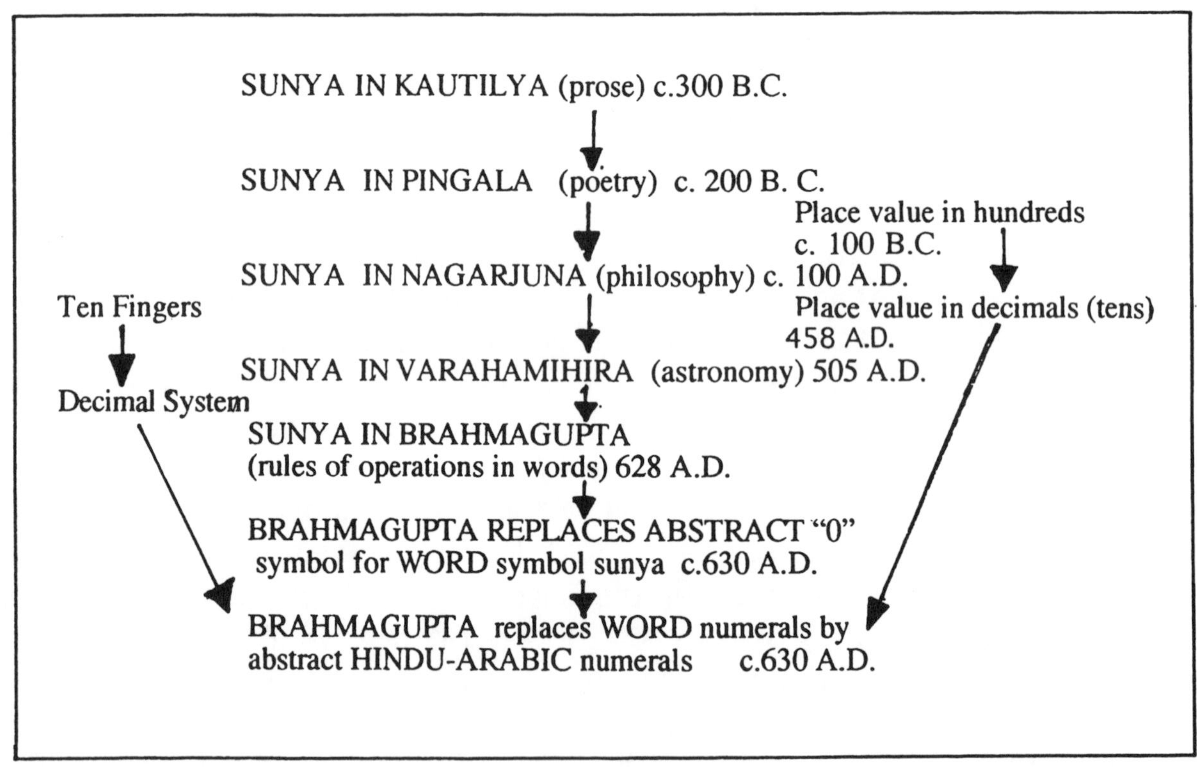

Fig. 17 A. SPREAD OF HINDU NUMERALS

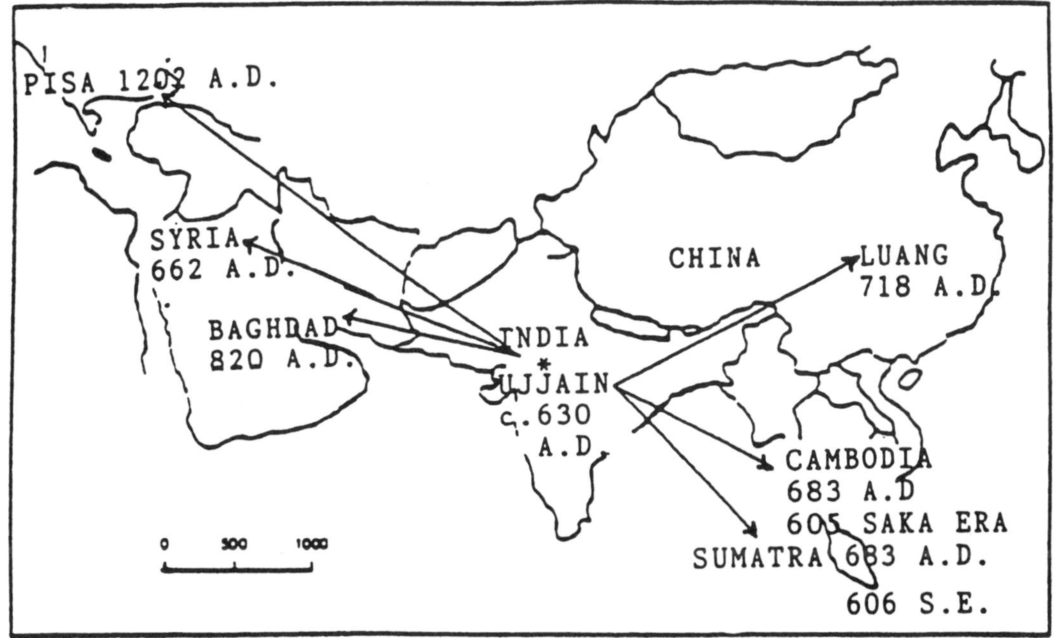

It is interesting to check the chronological spread of the Hindu numerals to different countries. The approximate date of the invention of the '0' and the Hindu numerals is 630 A.D., 32 years before the appearance of the Hindu numerals in Sebokht's writing, and 53 years in Southeast Asian countries. These duration of spread seems to be very reasonable. If Aryabhatta or Varahamihira, the two leading Indian mathematicians before Brahmagupta, invented the '0' or the Hindu numerals, the spread would not have taken over 184 years in the Southeast Asian countries.

Beginning in the fourth decade of the seventh century, the new numerals started replacing the old Indian numerals for calculations by all literate Indians and Southeast Asians. Professional mathematicians, however, continued to write their books on mathematics in verse for centuries for other scholars. The numerals spread 3,300 miles southeast of Ujjain, India, to the Hindu kingdoms of Southeast Asia. All the Southeast Asian countries had extensive trade and cultural relations during this period, and the new Indian numerals must have been a significant factor for prosperity on both sides. By increasing the speed of computation they facilitated commercial transactions, navigation, and recordkeeping in agricultural and industrial production and distribution. The prosperity of the Pallava and Chalukya of Vatapi in India, as well as in the Hindu Kingdoms of Southeast Asia such as Kambuja (Cambodia), Srivijaya (Sumatra), and Champa (South Vietnam) and, can be attributed to a significant extent to the numerals after the seventh century. As we have already mentioned, based on this prosperity the Cambodians were able to build the Hindu (Shiva) temple of Ankor Wat, one of the greatest architectural-sculptural masterpieces of the world. Around the later part of the first millennium, in Southeast Asia Hinduism was replaced by Buddism, preached by Indian monks; in India Buddhism was absorbed by Hinduism, and Buddha became a deity in the Hindu pantheon. In Java, Indonesia, the Indian influence led the Javanese to build the world's greatest Buddhist structure, the Stupa of Borobudor. The greatest temples in India, in Khajuraho, Konarak, and Belur-Halebid, were built between the ninth and twelfth centuries in Central, East, and South India, respectively. In Northern India repeated brutal invasions by Islamic hordes not only destroyed the Hindu temples but also devastated the economic, social, and cultural fabric for centuries. Though the manuscripts containing Indian numerals, and, of course, the dust boards have perished both in India and in Southeast Asia, some of the carvings on the rocks and the copperplate deeds still persist throughout the entire region. These carvings delineate the dates in the Saka era, originating during the Saka dynasty of India.

Did the numerals spread anywhere from Syria? The Greek mathematicians could hardly have taken the Indian numerals, as their civilization was already in decline. The Arabs could not have taken them either, since the Arabs were not yet advanced enough. The great Harun al Rashid (c. 800) established a sophisticated civilization centered in Bagdad. He and the next caliph encouraged scholars to come to Bagdad, and built a scholastic center based on the Arabic language. In addition, he arranged the translation of Sanskrit and Greek books into Arabic. In 820, Al Khowarezmi wrote a book in Arabic on the Hindu numerals in which he not only explained the numerals, but also displayed the techniques of addition, subtraction, multiplication, and division. As the Europeans took the Hindu numerals from the Arabs they named them the Arabic numerals.

It took many centuries before Indian numerals were accepted in Europe. For the Europeans, unlike the Southeast Asians, Indian culture was foreign and little known. Nonetheless, through the Arabs and, later, the Latin translation of Al Khowarezmi's book, the Indian numerals reached Europe by the tenth century; merchants and monastic scholars were the first to use them. One of the first European mathematicians who understood and used these numerals extensively was Fibonacci, the popular name of Leonardo of Pisa, the greatest mathematician of Europe between 300 and 1500. Fibonacci was born in Pisa when the city was very prosperous. With the help of his father, he traveled extensively around the Mediterranean countries and learned mathematics from a Moorish teacher. His book *Liber Abaci* (1202) was and remains today a landmark in the history of mathematics. Fibonacci was particularly impressed with the simplicity and elegance in computation with the nine symbols and the sign 0.

The Indian numerals spread slowly in Europe during the next three centuries. They had to compete with the abacus and the Roman numerals, which people already knew and in which they had confidence. They found the new numerals confusing, especially the zero, and wondered how a sign which meant nothing could increase the value of a number ten times by simply being placed after the number. Some Europeans thought it was the work of the devil, and actually named it so. Even so schools flourished, particularly in Italy, where students went to learn the new numerals. Bankers, merchants, and foreign traders who needed to calculate large numbers readily accepted the Hindu numerals. The transition over several centuries from the abacus and the Roman numerals to Indian numerals opened the door to suspicion and cheating. People did not write the symbols in the same way, causing further confusion. In several places the use of the new numerals was legally prohibited. Eventually, however, the numerals were accepted in all the countries of Europe, and by the15th century they were widely used.

Ifrah says, the "Hindu numerical system is as important as the invention of agriculture, the wheel, writing or the steam engine" (437). And Bell writes, "It is generally recognized that the Indian numerals are one of the greatest practical inventions of all times" (48). The Indian numerals expanded commercial activities, helping navigation and seaborne trade, and above all helped billions of people by simplifying calculations. The Indian numerals were among the essential elements in the prosperity of India and the Southeast Asian countries for several centuries. The effect of the Indian numerals on the European economy, commerce, navigation, and other aspects of civilization was even more spectacular. We first see the prosperity at first in the Italian cities and then throughout Europe.

The great French mathematician Pierre-Simon, Marquis de Laplace (1749-1827), observed:

> It is India that gave us the ingenious method of expressing all numbers by means of ten symbols, each symbol receiving a place-value as well as an absolute value, a profound and important idea which appears so simple to us now that we ignore its true merit. But its very simplicity and the great ease which it has lent to all computation put our arithmetic in the first rank

of useful invetions; and we shall appreciate the grandeur of this achievement the more when we remember that it escaped the genius of Archimedes and Apollonius, two of the greatest men produced by antiquity.

The failure of the Greeks and the Romans to devise an adequate numeral system delayed the growth of the Western civilization by centuries. One can only conjecture what would have happened had Brahmagupta not invented the Hindu numerals. Sixteenth and 17th century Europe would have continued to use Roman numerals and the abacus for calculations. The tremendous amount of complicated calculations needed for bankers, merchants, navigators and government officials would have been very difficult, even with many experts and extensive arithmetical tables. Some bright mathematician, perhaps in the 16th or the 17th century, might have suggested using Ptolemy's decimal-sexagesimal positionvalue numerals, much superior to the Roman numerals. As we have already seen, computation with Ptolemy's numerals was neither speedy nor easy compared to the Hindu numerals; it required numerous arithmetical tables as well as experts. Without the Hindu numerals economic growth in Europe would have been slower. With less wealth, there would have existed less support for the incomparable outburst of geniuses in Italy and, later, in other European countries during the Renaissance. The great series of brilliant European scientists and mathematicians since the 1a7th century would not have fully developed, or at least would have been delayed in such a relatively stagnant economic state. The Industrial Revolution might have been emasculated. Perhaps, some European mathematician would have taken the Babylonian-Greek sexagesimal-decimal numerals, and changed them to a consistant decimal system. This would have been a difficult task. As we know, modern astronomers still use a decimal-sexagesimal system. One of the greatest mathematicians of all time, Carl Friedrich Gauss (1777 -1855), realizing the greatness of the Indian numerals, once said regretfully about Archimedes, whom he greatly admired, "How could he have missed the discovery of our present positional system of writing our numerals? To what heights science would have risen by now, if only he had made that discovery" (Meninger, 141). The numerals have been used by all the great mathematicians and scientist of the world since Brahmagupta, and all of them have admired the notation system that made mathematics extremely efficient and useful for all. None of the great mathematicians - Descartes, Fermat, Newton, Leibniz, Euler, Lagrange, Gauss, Dedekind, and others - could replace them with an equal or better system of numerals, or even modify or improve on the Indian system.

One might ask why present-day India is in such a low level of economic development after having invented such a brilliant system. S. S. Bhatnagar, one of the leading contemporary Indian scientists, has commented, "We invented the ten digit numeral system, but we kept only the zero, and gave the numerals to the West!" With the Indian numerals, Europe, North America and Japan have flourished, leaving India struggling with poverty and hardship. Basking in the glory of their forefathers' inventions is not enough to elevate any civilization. However, recent economic trends suggest that India may be already on the way to accelerated growth; the country has large number of skilled people, a large middle class, an extensive market, and a free economy. Only a war or preparation for wars could cut short the development.

A nearby small hill looks higher than a distant mountain. We are often dazzled by, and overestimate the performance of our own century, and lose perspective on the preceding 5,000 years of civilization. It often takes centuries to estimate the total impact of a fundamental creation in relation to our civilization. Over 1,365 years later, with constant worldwide use of the numerals, the luster of the invention has been lost but not its extreme importance and utility. This is the saga of our numerals. There is no other mathematical invention that has been so useful and widely known to all humanity. It remains a part of us from early childhood to the end of our lives.

NEGATIVE NUMBERS

The people of Sumer and Egypt recorded loss or debt, which were concrete and physical phenomenan, not abstract negative numbers. Chinese negative numbers are discussed in the chapter on Chinese arithmetic.

After the invention of the zero, Brahmagupta (628) probably recognized, that the positive numbers start from the zero and extend to infinity, and conversely, that the negative numbers also begin at the zero and extend in the opposite direction to infinity. Without the concept of zero as a number, he probably could not have invented abstract negative numbers. Of course, metrological (measurement) negative numbers do not require any concept of the zero. The close relationship between these two great abstract concepts, namely, the zero and the negative numbers, was obvious to Brahmagupta as he formulated their rules of operation together, and probably, he invented both of them in one of the supreme flights of genius the world has ever known. He provided for the negative numbers the four basic rules of operation and an abstract symbol (a dot on the top of the negative numbers), which all numbers must have. One may say that a number of any type in the negative field is a negative number. Geometrical figures, of course, could also be in the negative field or space.

It is indeed surprising that this abstract concept is so useful in mathematics, science, engineering, economics, finance and other fields. Without it a fully developed arithmetic, algebra, analytic geometry, calculus, vector analysis, modern trigonometry, and many other branches of mathematics would be impossible. The Imaginary numbers also developed from Brahmagupta's negative numbers.

Brahmagupta provided a rule for the square root of the zero. Why did he not next provide the rule for the square root of negative numbers? The zero is much more abstract than negative numbers. Mahavira (850) and Bhaskara (1150) accepted negative numbers but stated, there is no square root of negative quantity for it is not a square. Al Khowarizmi (820) and most of the Arab mathematicians except Omar Khayyam accepted the negative and other numbers from India in good faith, and passed them on to Europe. Many great European mathematicians, for example, Descartes, Fermat and Pascal, did not accept negative numbers. Euler, perhaps the greatest mathematician of the 18th century, believed that the negative numbers were greater than infinity.

During the Italian Renaissance, Cardano (1545) added and subtracted two square roots of the negative numbers, creating the imaginary number, although he called it a meaningless, fictitious, impossible, and mystical (Dantzig,182). Newton did not accept negative numbers since they had no physical or geometrical reality. It was Leibniz who philosophized them as the amphibian between being and nonbeing, and named them the imaginary number.

IRRATIONAL NUMBERS

When we seek the square root of 2, 3 , 5, 6, 7, 8 and most other whole numbers we get irrational numbers. For example the square root of 2 is 1. 414214 ......They are named irrational numbers, not because they are crazy, but because they are not ratios of two whole numbers. In contrast, the unit fractions are ratios of two whole numbers. The decimals of the irrationals are nonrepeating and interminable; they have "continuity." Babylonians were the first to face irrational numbers while trying to square root the number 2. However, they approximated them with their sexagesimal fraction, and then calculated with their approximated fractions, thus bypassing the irrationals. Overreacting when they discovered that the square root of 2 was not a ratio of two whole numbers, the Pythagorians avoided them. Although Euclid showed his genius in his work on irrationals, he did not accept them as numbers, and instead pushed them into geometry. This was clearly a mistake since geometry, with only a rudimentary ability to compute, is a poor tool to handle numbers. "The Greek's inability to grasp the concept of irrational numbers," Kline comments, "not only retarded the development of Greek arithmetic and algebra but also hindered later generations to develop them" (1972, p. 173).

Brahmagupta (628) was the first mathematician who accepted the irrationals as a different type of genuine numbers, and he gave the "rules of addition and subtraction on irrationals" (Colebrooke, 340); however, his results were incorrect. Bhaskara (1150) devoted a whole section in his book to irrational numbers with examples of addition, subtraction, multiplication, and division. His formula for addition and subtraction for the irrationals is used today in our algebra texts for finding a square root of a binomial surd (Eves,18; Dantzig,109). The Arabs took the irrational numbers from India and called them inaudible *(surd)*, and passed them to Europe. Napier (1617), the inventor of logarithm, found them necessary in the use of the logarithmic scale. Most 17th century mathematicians, for example, Stiffel and Pascal, failed to accept them as numbers, while others such as Descartes and Fermat had no clear idea of them (Kline, c.114). Richard Dedekind explained them by an apparently simple but very ingenious method (cut) in his "Continuity and Irrationals" (1872). Today, Irrational numbers are used extensively in many branches of mathematics and science, engineering and technology.

PASCAL'S TRIANGLE

1

1 1

1 2 1

1 3 3 1

1 4 6 4 1

1 5 10 10 5 1

1 6 15 20 15 6 1

1 7 21 35 35 21 7 1

The arithmetical triangle associated with the great mathematician Blaise Pascal's name was first mentioned by Varahamihira (505 A.D.). He explained the poet Pingala's method (200 B.C.): "the numbers are obtained by adding each with the one which is passed to the one in front of it, except the one in last place" (Hughes, 213). Halayudha in the tenth century presented the triangle (Hofmann, v. I, 93) and named it *Meru-prastar.*

Each number is the sum of the two numbers above it. If we toss a coin four times, the possibilities can be found from the fifth line, 1/16, 4/16, 6/16 and 4/16 of the possible outcome of 16. The Chinese mathematician Chia Hsien (c.1050) (Libbrecht,18), and the Persian poet-mathematician Omar Khayyam (c. 1100), studied it. This is the basis of probability and statistics. Blaise Pascal and Pierre de Fermat (c.1630) greatly improved upon it. Nowadays it is difficult to find any aspect of human endeavor and activities where probabability and statistics are not used.

INFINITY AND INFINITESIMAL

Bhaskara, II (1150 A.D.) wrote that "the product of a (number and) zero is kha-guna; his commentator Krishna explained that "the more the multiplicand is diminished, the smaller the product; and if it be reduced in the utmost degree, the product is so likewise, [and] now the utmost quantity is the same as with the reduction of it to nothing." Here Bhaskara conceived the smallest quantity leading to the zero, the infinitesimal. The idea of the infinite first appeared in the philosophical poem the *Upanishad* (about eighth century B.C.): "Taking infinity (*purna* =totality) from infinity [still] infinity remains." Bhaskara,II, also stated, "In this quantity consisting of that which has cipher for its divisor, there is no alteration, although many may be inserted or extracted; as no change takes place in the infinite and immutable God at the period of creation or the destruction of the worlds, though numerous orders of being is absorbed or put forth" (Datta & Singh, v.1, 243). Indian mathematicians' idea of numbers at Bhaskara, II's time:

Negative Positive
Infinity,....-trillions,....-10000... ,0, infinitesimal.... trillions,........Infinity
______________________________|______________________________

XI. CHINESE ARITHMETIC

The earliest example of Chinese arithmetic is preserved on the oracle bones at a time before 1,200 B. C. Our knowledge of the development of arithmetic for the next thousand years suffers due to the despotic ruler Shih Hoang Ti, who in 213 B. C. ordered the incineration of all books and the burial alive of all the scholars.

In China the most famous and enduring work of mathematics is the *Nine Chapters of Mathematical Arts (Chiu-Chang Suan-Shu).* This is a collection of works by different mathematicians over probably a few centuries. The book was collected in the first or second century A.D. This classic had a tremendous influence on the Chinese, Korean and Japanese mathematicians for well over 1,000 years, and during the T'ang and Song Dynasties (618-1213) it was a standard textbook. All the old manuscripts and most copies of the famous book are lost. The earliest extant copy is from the early thirteen century A.D. It is woodblock printed and contains only five sections out of the nine. The rest of the book was reconstructed in the late eighteenth century, based on a Chinese encyclopedia of the 15th century, the *Yong le da Dian*. Only part of it exists today. The *Nine Chapters on the Mathematical Arts* was not recorded in the *Book of Arts and Crafts* in the History of the Han Dynasty (206 B.C. to 220 A.D). Liu Hui (263 A.D.), Lu Cheng Feng of the T'ang Dynasty (618-907), and many others "collated and commented on the book, they did not make a lot of changes on it," comments Yan and Shiran (p.36). They also state, "At the latest by the First Century A.D. *the Nine Chapters on the Mathematical Art* had been written in the form we now have." It is a wonder how Yan and Shiran could know that the original book has not changed much when no manuscripts or their copies exist before the 13th century A.D.!

The contents of the *Nine Chapters of the Mathematical Arts* are varied. The first three chapters are concerned with the measurements of the cultivated land, and the exchange and distribution of cereals. In chapters 4 and 5, methods are discussed to find the square roots as well as the volume of various solid shapes. Chapter 6 is about calculations related to the distribution of grain and corvee labor. In the next chapter, the method of "false position" for solving problems on contributions, purchasing, etc. are explained. Chapter 8 deals with problems on simultaneous linear equations. This method of calculation is known as the method of rectangular arrays because of the way the counting rods are arranged. The concepts of positive and negative numbers and the method of calculating their sums and differences are also introduced in this chapter. According to Yan &

Shiran (48), the original text says: *"The method of positive and negative states: for subtracting - same signs take away, different signs add together, positive from nothing makes negative, negative from nothing makes positive; for addition - different signs take away, same signs add together., positive and nothing is positive, negative and nothing makes negative."* Yan and Shiran (49) go further, and in interpolating the zero, explain in "modern terms," that "taking a positive number from zero gives a negative number, taking a negative number from zero gives positive number....adding a positive number to zero gives a positive, adding a negative number to zero gives a negative."

As only a part of the copy of the mathematical classic was found in the thirteenth century, is there any interpolation during these twelve centuries? This is similar to the Indian *Bakhshali* manuscript which has had some interpolation over the centuries. Mikami (p.21) believes that the Chinese had negative numbers but not the zero. The greatest expert on China in the West, Sir Joseph Needham states (v. 3, p. 9) that before the eighth century, the place where a zero is required was always left vacant; for example, in the Tunghuang cave-temples, where there is a multiplication table in which the results appear both in written form and as rod-numerals, 405 was written as IIII IIIII. Needham continues that he never came across the zero in any mathematical text earlier than Ming (1368-1644), though the Sung (960-1279) algebraists used the symbol O extensively (ibid,16). However, with regard to negative numbers, Professor Needham's opinion is that "negative numbers were known in the *Suan Shu Chiu Chang* or at least as early as Li Hui (+3rd century). Brahmagupta may well have invented them independently" (Needham, Personal correspondence, Dec, 2, 90).

Regarding the quotation from the Yan and Shiran's book (49) on the computation with the zero and the negative numbers, Professor Martzloff, the author of *Histoire de Mathematique Chinoise* (1987), writes: "The correctness of the English rendering of this quotation seems to me doubtful because the Chinese text has not a word corresponding to what is rendered here as 'zero' (this 'zero' is perhaps the translation of *wu* a word meaning here 'there is not' ["if there is nothing to be (added) resp. subtracted..."]) (Personal correspondence, Nov 22,1990). The thirteenth century outburst of Chinese mathematics with numerals with a zero, the negative numbers, all in abstract symbols, and extensive use in computation almost certainly did not come from the elementary ideas over thousand years earlier. Mikami (59) thinks that the Chinese zero in the thirteenth century came from India.

The golden age of Chinese mathematics lasted only 56 years (1247-1303 A.D.). During this short period three of the greatest Chinese mathematicians appeared. Chin Chiu Shao wrote the *Nine Sections of Mathematics* in 1247. While serving in the army he was disabled, and after retirement he studied astronomy, music, poetry, art and architecture. He was the first Chinese mathematician to use the symbol O for zero, which was certainly borrowed from an Indian source, perhaps through the Chinese translation of the Chiu-Chi-Li (Mikami,73). The solution of numerical higher equation for approximate value, which is considered to be the most characteristic of Chinese mathematics, culminated in Ch'in Chiu-Shao's works. This was reinvented by Ruffini (1802) and by Horner in 1819. Needham (vol. 3,p.126), however, comments that the treatment by Ruffini and Horner was recondite and intricate, involving higher analysis as well as elementary algebra, and is used today in algebraic textbooks. Ch'in Chiu-Shao also invented the method of putting only the '0' on one side of the equation, which we now call Harriot's (b.1560) method; it is used extensively today. Ch'in Chiu-Shao invented a method of expressing decimal fractions in words. For example, fen for 0.1, li for 0.01, hau for 0.001....yen for 0.000000000001. His *Precious Mirror of the Four Elements* is one of the outstanding books of medieval times of the world. Li Yeh, who published the book *Sea Mirror of the Circle Movement,* was the first Chinese mathematician to give the rules on negative numbers in symbols. Chu Shih Chien published *The Introduction to Mathematical Studies* in 1299, generalized the technique of the higher degree numerical equations to four unknowns.

XII. CULTURAL EXCHANGE BETWEEEN INDIA AND CHINA

We may review the spread of Chinese culture to other countries and *vice versa*, specifically in the realm of mathematics before the Renaissance. There are many misinformations on this subject. One has to remember that independent contemporary invention of the same mathematical concepts is not uncommon, for example, Newton and Leibniz on calculus, and Lobachevky, Gauss, and Bolyai on non-Euclidian geometry. Although Gauss and Bolyai knew each other, they still invented independently. So to show that some aspects of culture is transmitted to another culture in ancient times should be based on solid evidence.

In the first section of this book we showed the overwhelming influence of the Indian Brahmi alphabet and Indian culture on most of Asia. The spread of Chinese culture, including mathematics, to Korea and Japan is also well-known and documented. Surprisingly, Chinese civilization had virtually no influence on its southern neighbors, including Burma, Thai-land, Laos, South Vietnam, Sumatra, Java, and Bali. The only exception is North Vietnam. It is an even greater surprise to see very little Chinese cultural influence on Tibet, Nepal, and Bhutan. On the other hand, all these countries adapted Indian culture thoroughly. Hinduism dominated the religious lives of Southeast Asians for most of the first millennium (Coedes). Then, in the later part of the first millennium, the Indian Buddhist monks converted the Hindus of South-east Asia to Buddhism. The Southeast Asians took from India their literature (Indian epics, Ramayana and Mahabharata), architecture, sculpture, painting (Rawlinson, Groslier, Krom), philosophy, dance, and almost all other aspects of civilization. All these influences are well documented, and even today we see the results all over the area.

India's influence on China has been notable. We have extensive evidence that since the first century, Indian Buddhist monks spread Buddhism throughout China. The monks translated into Chinese a great deal of Buddhistic literature from Pali, the earlier language of the Buddhist scripture, and from Sanskrit. As Mikami writes, during the fifth and sixth centuries:

> The Indian works were read in translation ten times more than the Chinese classics a fact that vividly tells how the Indian influence had swept over the country. Things Indian exercised supremacy in art and literature, in philosophy, in the mode of life and the thoughts of the inhabitants in everything....How then could arithmetic remain alone unaffected? No doubt the Chinese studied the arithmetical works of the Hindoos (p. 57).

The Indian artists also took Indian sculpture to China, as evidenced by the great figure of Buddha in stone in Yun Kang dating around 490, the gallery of the serene Buddha and other pieces of sculpture in Lung-Men in Central China and the paintings of Buddha and the stories associated with him, during the T'ang Dynasty. The Indian art provided the impetus, ennobling spirit, the subject, the style, and for enlightened Chinese masters to create great art, as had occurred among the Cambodians and the Javanese. The borrowing never deteriorated into the superficial Greco-Buddhic art of Gandhara or Roman art.

Not a single Chinese scholar went to India to teach the wisdom of Confucius or Lao-Tze, nor did any Chinese artist go there with the art of ceramic or landscape painting. No Chinese astronomer or mathematician visited India to learn and teach. In contrast, the Indian astronomers monopolized the astronomical laboratories of China, as Schafer (p.128) attested, during the T'ang Dynasty (618 - 906). Many Chinese Buddhist scholar-monks came to their holy land, India, to learn about the religion and to collect Buddhist scriptures to be translated into Chinese. They were well received in India; in fact, the kings vied with each other to have the scholars adorn their courts. Many of these Buddhist monks were not only knowledgeable about their religion but were also keen observers of the political, social, and economical situation in India. Some of them, for example, Fa Hien (who returned to China in 414), and particularly Huen Shang, (who lived in India from 629 to 645) kept extremely valuable records without which the social history of India would be incomplete. However, not a single book mentioned mathematics. The majority of the Indian Buddhist missionaries, astronomers, artists and traders, who went to China settled there permanently. Those who returned to India did not bring any aspect of Chinese culture that has been recorded in Indian or Chinese literature.

When a great civilization was built in Baghdad in the 730s, many Indian astronomers went to Bagdad to teach astronomy and mathematics. Numerous books were translated from Sanskrit into Arabic, including Brahmagupta's *Zij al-sindhind.* Astronomical treaties based on the Indian astronomy were written (Berggren,2). Indian mathematics flowed to Baghdad freely, and Al khowarezmi in 820 wrote a book on Hindu numerals showing the method of calculation using them. There is no evidence of Chinese scholars in the courts of Bagdad caliphs, nor any translation of Chinese books into Arabic during the height of the Islamic civilization. In the Yuan times (Mongols1271-1368), "the Persians, Central Asians and the Arabs played a role in Chinese science and technology quite similar to the Indians in the T'ang Dynasty" (618-906) (Needham, 49).

To summarize, although Chinese culture spread to Japan, Korea and North Vietnam, it had little or no influence on India, the Southeast Asian countries, Tibet, or Nepal. Communication between China and the Arab world started much later, only when the Mongolians occupied Baghdad (Yan and Shiran, 173). We have solid evidence from the Chinese sources that the Indians carried Hindu astronomy and mathematics along with many aspects of their civilization. In contrast, there is not a single piece of evidence that the Chinese or the returning Indians from China brought to India any significant aspect of Chinese culture, including mathematics. Along with Buddhism, Indian culture penetrated the breadth and depth of hundreds of millions of Chinese minds. Unfortunately, the best Chinese ideas and culture did not reach India until after the European Renaissance. Only then through Europe did India acquire paper, movable type, compass, gunpowder, ceramic vases, landscape painting, and other Chinese creations.

XIII. MAYAN ARITHMETIC

The Mayans developed a major original civilization which included large pyramids, sculptures, a writing system, brilliant numerals, astronomy, and a highly sophisticated and accurate calender. They showed their genius by inventing the place-value system as well as an abstract sign for the zero represented by a seashell ( ). It seems that they first invented "named" place-value system from which the place-value in abstract symbols developed, similar to India. Mayans used vegisimal units (20) so they could use 1 to 19 for each place; in contrast, in the decimal system we can use 1 to 9 for each position. Unfortunately, in astronomical calculations the Mayans used in the third position of their place-value system 18 instead of 20, making calculation difficult in this mixed units. However, their structures of place-values are otherwise similar to ours. For example,

8 katuns 7 tuns 13 uinals 5 kins = (8x7200)+(7x360)+ (13x20) +5 = 60,385
8 sahasra 7 satam 9 dasam 5 = (8x1000) + (7x100) + (9x10) + 5 = 8, 795

Like the Babylonians, Mayans could write any large number with only three symbols. Their symbols were a dot for one, a line for five, placed horizontally or vertically, and used in additive principle. For example, • • • or ⋮ for 3, __ for 5, ••• for 8, and a seashell ( ) for the '0'.

Mayan civilization stretches back to almost 1,000 B.C.; mathematics reached its highest level from the beginning of the classical period starting around 300 A.D; it decayed after c. 900.

XIV. ARAB ARITHMETIC

The first great mathematician was Al Khowarezmi, whose first book survives in Latin translation, *Algoritmi de numero Indorum* (820) (Computation with Indian numbers), where he explains the great advantages of Indian numerals in computation. Al Khowarezmi's greatness lies as does Fibonacci's, in his absorbing new, superior, and foreign concepts which not only improved mathematics but also greatly helped economic growth. Economic prosperity helped all aspects of civilization. Al Khwarezmi also contributed the name algebra, *Tarik aljebr wa almukabala* meaning the method of restoration and comparison. However, he did not invent algebra as some mathematicians mistakenly wrote, but took algebra from Aryabhatta and Brahmagupta. Algebra was first used by the Sumerians and Babylonians. Abul-Hasan al-Uqlidisi, the writer of the Book, *Chapters on Hindu Arithmetic* (952) was the first mathematician to invent the decimal fraction with a decimal 'point.' He gave a much better sign for the decimal 'point,' a short straight line above the first number, 0'59375 (Berggren, 37) than had Stevin (1590) over six hundred years earlier. After this period, economic decline, along with religious intolerance, limited mathematics and other aspects of civilization.

XV. OBSERVATIONS ON TRANSMISSION OF CULTURE AND MATHEMATICS

The spread of mathematics from one culture to another superficially resemble a madman's journey. However, there is a method, like Hamlet's, to this madness. As we have shown that mathematicians may independently and simultaneously develop the same concept in the same culture. The most famous example was the independent discovery of calculus by Newton and Leibniz, causing unpleasant controversy as to the priority. Other examples of independent inventions are Descartes' and Fermat's analytic geometry, the projective geometry of Desargue and Pascal, and probability by Pascal and Fermat. It is likely that in ancient times, with slow transport, limited communication, great physical barriers, unknown languages and culture, few travellers, most of whom were traders and religious missionaries with little interest in mathematics, that dissemination of mathematics would have been severely restricted, resulting in various independent inventions in diferrent and distant cultures.

However, the facts only partially correlate to this reasoning. The spread of mathematics, like other aspects of culture, mainly depends on the energy and determination of the voyagers of nations who are brave enough to cross high mountains, long deserts, and rough oceans to spread their culture: religion, philosophy, art, language and literature as well as scripts, science and mathematics. The acceptance of one culture by another culture depends mainly on the attitude of the borrowing people towards the donating people and their culture, and not on any physical, linguistic, or cultural barriers. This applies to the ancient period and, to a less extent, to modern times, and is true with almost all aspects of culture.

The Greeks had great regard for the ancient Egyptians, and they absorbed much of their wisdom, including their mathematics. However, they rejected the superior arithmetic of the Babylonians with whom they had often close contact, throughout the duration of their civilization. The Chinese considered even the southern Chinese, the Man people, as semi-barbarians, and they considered all others as fully barbaric. They did not go to other lands to spread their culture, nor took any active role in the spread of their own culture. The Koreans took the initiative and absorbed almost all aspects of Chinese civilization. It was also the Koreans who took Chinese culture to Japan. Later the Japanese went to China to learn firsthand about Chinese civilization. The Mongols conquered Baghdad and established cultural communications between the Arabs and the Chinese. After the Renaissance the Europeans established their colonies on the seaports of China, spreading their culture and taking from the Chinese many features of their civilization. In contrast, Indian monks crossed the high mountains and long deserts, and carried the teaching of Buddha. These were first accepted by the northern elites of China, and later spead to the rest of the people. After that, many facets of Indian civilization were taken by the Chinese, as we have already discussed. Indian numerals spread to Cambodia, 3,300 miles away, within only five decades of their origin because the Southeast Asian people held Indian culture in high esteem. As a result, they absorbed the Indian alphabet, religion, literature, architecture, sculpture, dance and other arts. It took almost 1,000 years for the Europeans to accept the Indian arithmetic and algebra, for they long retained the Roman numerals and abacus. Culture, of course, spreads with military conquest, and particularly with colonization. Two well-known examples are the Roman culture which spread to most of Europe, North Africa, and West Asia; and the Arabic culture, which spread to the Mediterranean area, much of Western and Central Asia as well as Iran, Pakistan and India.

There were selective borrowings from one culture to another; for example, astronomy, probably because of its association with astrology and religion, spread easily. India took Greek astronomy along with the geometry and trigonometry. Algebra travelled poorly, for the Greeks took little of Babylonian algebra. Babylonian and Greek algebra did not influence the Indians much, and the Arabs took little of Indian algebra.

We can summarize the contribution of the ancient arithmetic in the words of one of the leading historian of mathematics, Florian Cajori:

> It is remarkable to what extent Indian mathemaitcs enters into the science of our time. Both the form and the spirit of the

arithmetic and algebra of modern times are essentially Indian. Think of our notation of numbers, brought to perfection by the Hindus, think of the arithmetical operations nearly as perfect as our own, think of their elegant algebraic methods (97).

REFERENCES

Aryabhatta, *The Aryabhatiya,* translated by W. Eugene, Chicago, 1930

Bell, E. T. *The Development of mathematics.* New York, 1940,

Berggren, J.L., *Episodes in the mathematics of Medieval Islam*, New York, 1986

Brahmagupta, *Brahma-Sphuta-Siddhanta* Tr. Henry T. Colebrooke, London, 1817

Bhaskara, *Bhaskara Siddhanta Siromoni.* .Tr. Henry T. Colebrook, London,1817

Burton, David M., *The History of Mathematics*, Dubuque, Iowa, 1985

Boyer, Carl B., *A History of Mathematics*, 2nd Ed., New York

Cajori, Florian, *A History of Mathematics,* 1980

Dantzig, Tobias, *Numbers:The Language of Science*, New York, 1954

Datta, B.B. & Singh A.N., *A History of Hindu mathematics*, Bombay,1962

Eves, Howard, *An Introduction to the History of Mathematics*, N. Y,1983

Gupta, R.C., *Ganita Bharati*, vol. 12, No.1-2, p.23, New Delhi. 1990.

Halstead, G.B., *On the Foundation and Technique of Arithmetic*, Chicago, 1912

Hayashi, Takao, *The Bakhshali Manuscript*, Thesis, Brown Univ., R.I.,1985

Hofmann. Joseph, *The History of Mathematics to 1800*, 2 vols, 1967

Hughes, Barnabas, *Historia Mathematica* v.6, 213, 1989

Ifrah, Georges, *From One to Zero,* N. Y., 1985.

Kline, Morris. *Mathematics a Cultural Approach*, Reading, Mass. 1962

" ' *Mathematical Thought from the Ancient to Modern Times,* N.Y.1972

Li Yan and Du Shiran, *Chinese Mathematics, A concise history*, Oxford, 1987

Linn, Charles F., *Ages of Mathematics*: vol.2, *Mathematics East and West,* N.Y. 1977

Meninger, Karl, *Number Words and Number Symbols,* Camb., Mass, 1969

Mikami, Yoshio, *The Development of Mathematics in China and Japan,* New York,1919

Mukherjee, R.N., *Discovery of Zero and Its Impact.* Calcutta, 1991

Needham, Joseph, *Science and Civilization in China,* vol, 3,

mathematics, Cambridge, England, 1954
Neugebauer, Otto, *The Exact Sciences of the Antiquity*, Providence, R.I,1957
Russell, Bertrand, *Introduction to Mathematical Philosophy*, London, 1920
Schafer, Edward H., *Ancient China*, N. Y.,1967
Smith, D. E., *History of Mathematics*, 2 vols, N. Y. 1951
Smith, D. E. and Karpinski, *The Hindu Arabic Numerals*, Boston, Mass, 1911
Struik, D. J., Ed., *A Source Book in Mathematics, 1200-1800* , Cambridge, Mass. 1969.
Varahamihira, *Panca-Siddhantika,* Calcutta, n.d.